New
Music
Horizons

McCONATHY

MORGAN

MURSELL

BARTHOLOMEW

BRAY

MIESSNER

BIRGE

Sixth Book

ILLUSTRATED BY JULES GOTLIEB

SILVER BURDETT COMPANY

NEW YORK   CHICAGO   SAN FRANCISCO

ACKNOWLEDGMENTS

...ors for their interest and coopera-
tion that space prohibits individual ... ...eir valued contribution.

To the following composers, poets, and publishers from whom source materials have
been secured, credit and appreciation are due:

The American Folklore Society, Inc., for "Dancing" from *Memoirs*, Vol. 10.

Marion Bergman for "Polka."

Brandt & Brandt for "Lewis and Clark" from *A Book of Americans*, copyright, 1933, by Rosemary and Stephen Vincent Benét, published by Farrar & Rinehart, Inc.; "Afternoon on a Hill," copyright, 1917, by Edna St. Vincent Millay, from *Renascence and Other Poems* published by Harper & Brothers.

Cultural, S.A., Havana, for "They're Arguing Still" from *Rondas Escolares Para Los Grados Primarios* by Yolanda Lleonart, Andres de Piedra-Bueno, and Arturo R. Ojea.

The estate of Stella Marek Cushing for selected materials from Bulgaria, Czechoslovakia, Greece, Poland, Russia, and Yugoslavia.

Oliver Ditson Company, copyright owners, for "Desert Song," "In Days of Old," and "My Lovely Maiden" from *100 Folk Songs of All Nations*, edited and arranged by Bantock; "Serenade" from *60 Folk Songs of France* by Tiersot.

Dodd, Mead & Co. for permission to reprint "Daisies" from *Songs of Vagabondia* by Bliss Carman, copyright, by Dodd, Mead & Co.

E. P. Dutton & Co., Inc., for "Garden Song" from *Gaily the Troubadour* by Arthur Guiterman, published and copyright, 1936.

Eleanor Farjeon for "The Swallows Are Homing."

Harper & Brothers for "Telling Time" from *The Cheery Way*, copyright, 1920, by John Kendrick Bangs.

Fjeril Hess and Lilian Jackson for "Shusti-Fidli" from *Sing Together* by permission of Girl Scouts, National Organization.

Imprenta Nacional, San José, Costa Rica, for "The Ugly Duckling" from *Coleccion de Canciones y Danzas Típicas*.

Dorothy M. Kahananui for "Prayer of Shipwrecked Men," from *The Music Hour, Hawaiian edition*, published by Silver Burdett Company.

Charles E. King for the English translation of "Aloha Oe."

Alexander Koshetz for "Autumn" and "Lazy Laddie."

Mildred Loper for "Samoan Boat Song," from *The Music Hour, Hawaiian edition*, published by Silver Burdett Company.

The Macmillan Company for "A Swing Song" from *Robin Redbreast and Other Verses* by William Allingham.

John and Evelyn McCutcheon for "The Pirate Ship" from *The Island Song Book*.

Kate Taylor Parmley for the traditional version of "Git Along, Little Dogies!"

Manuel M. Ponce for "Palomita."

The Reilley & Lee Co. for permission to use "A Patriotic Creed" from *Poems of Patriotism* by Edgar A. Guest, copyright, 1922.

Francisca Reyes-Tolentino for "The Meadow Butterfly," from *The Progressive Music Series, Philippine Edition*, published by Silver Burdett Company.

G. Ricordi & Co., Inc., copyright owners, for "Mother's Advice" from *I Canti Bella Montagna* and "My Dog and I" from *Songs for Children*, Vol. I.

The estate of Luis Sandoval for "Parting."

Charles Scribner's Sons for "Dear Land of All My Love" from *Centennial Ode* by Sidney Lanier.

Jean Thomas, the "Traipsin' Woman," and Joseph A. Leeder for "Down in the Valley" from *The Singin' Gatherin'*, published by Silver Burdett Company.

Frances Toor for "Fiesta" from *Cancionero Mexicano*, copyright, 1931.

Nancy Byrd Turner for "Washington."

H. Villa-Lobos for "Fashions" from *Guia Pratico*.

Henri Wehrmann for "Baked Potato."

The estate of Carolyn Wells for "The Big Bazaar" ("The Animals' Fair").

Anne Williams for "Willow Whistles" and "Homesick."

Yale University Press for "Tending the Sheep" from *Folk Songs of French Canada* by Marius Barbeau and Edward Sapir.

Young Judaea for "Praise the Lord" from the *Judaean Songster*.

For special services, grateful acknowledgment is made to the following:

Lillian L. Baldwin, Alice C. Cooper, Charles and Ruth Seeger, and Lota M. Spell.

Bertha Donner, Rafael Fenili, Marjut Klase, Virginia Kracke, Eva Markov, James S. McConathy, Hannah Nolander, Sylvia M. Pond, Marguerite Rhonan, for English translations of foreign language texts.

Edna W. Doll, Department of Physical Education, Clifford J. Scott High School, East Orange, New Jersey, for the organization and activities in rhythmic activities.

Δ

NEW MUSIC HORIZONS

Sixth Book

National Hymn

D. C. ROBERTS

GEORGE W. WARREN

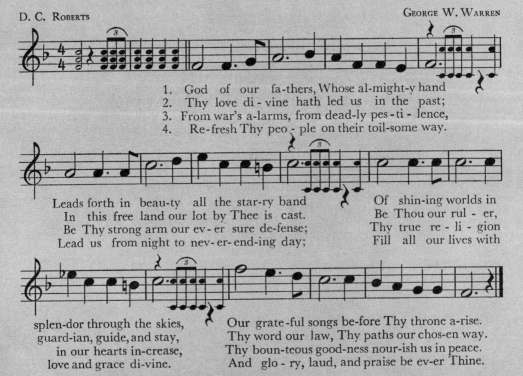

1. God of our fa-thers, Whose al-might-y hand
2. Thy love di-vine hath led us in the past;
3. From war's a-larms, from dead-ly pes-ti-lence,
4. Re-fresh Thy peo-ple on their toil-some way.

Leads forth in beau-ty all the star-ry band | Of shin-ing worlds in
In this free land our lot by Thee is cast. | Be Thou our rul - er,
Be Thy strong arm our ev - er sure de-fense; | Thy true re - li - gion
Lead us from night to nev-er-end-ing day; | Fill all our lives with

splen-dor through the skies, | Our grate-ful songs be-fore Thy throne a-rise.
guard-ian, guide, and stay, | Thy word our law, Thy paths our chos-en way.
in our hearts in-crease, | Thy boun-teous good-ness nour-ish us in peace.
love and grace di-vine. | And glo - ry, laud, and praise be ev-er Thine.

iv

Bb Trumpets and Clarinets

Warren's NATIONAL HYMN was written to celebrate the 100th anniversary of the signing of the Declaration of Independence.

1

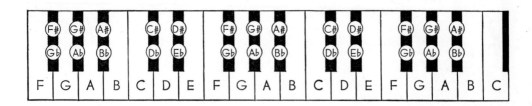

THE PIANO KEYBOARD

One of the simplest ways to show the relationship of tones is by means of the piano keyboard or a set of bells. As you have already learned, the first seven letters of the alphabet are used as pitch names for the different tones, and these letters are also used to name the white keys on the piano. The black keys take their names from the neighboring white keys. "Sharp" means one half-step higher, and "flat" means one half-step lower. A half-step is from any key to its nearest neighboring key, black or white, and may be indicated by ⌣.

A scale is a series of tones from any given tone to the next higher or lower tone having the same name, that is, from C to C, or from G to G, from E-flat to E-flat, and so forth. In the major scale, this series is organized by steps and half-steps, as follows:

Try playing the major scale on the piano, starting at different places. You will soon discover that different combinations of white and black keys must be played to make the scale sound right according to the above plan of steps and half-steps.

The Scale in the Key of C

Scale Numbers:	5	6	7	8	1	2	3	4	5	6	7	8	2	3	4	5
Pitch Names:	G	A	B	C	D	E	F	G	A	B	C	D	E	F	G
Syllables:	so	la	ti	do	re	mi	fa	so	la	ti	do	re	mi	fa	so

Swing the Sickle

(Two-part Round)

MARY BUDLONG   KARL HERING

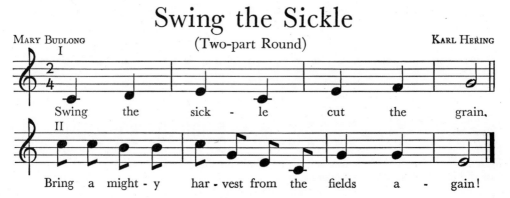

I

Swing   the   sick - le   cut   the   grain,

II

Bring   a   might - y   har - vest from   the   fields   a - gain!

They're Arguing Still

Translated from the SPANISH by
NANCY BYRD TURNER

FOLK SONG from CUBA

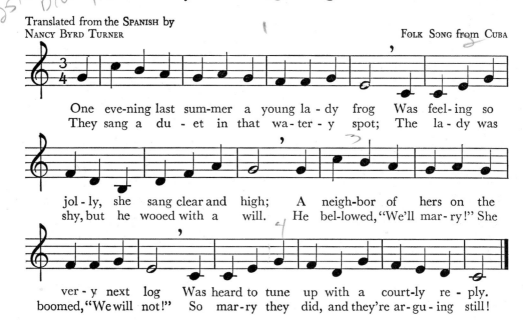

One eve-ning last sum-mer a young la-dy frog Was feel-ing so
They sang a du-et in that wa-ter-y spot; The la-dy was

jol-ly, she sang clear and high; A neigh-bor of hers on the
shy, but he wooed with a will. He bel-lowed, "We'll mar-ry!" She

ver-y next log Was heard to tune up with a court-ly re-ply.
boomed, "We will not!" So mar-ry they did, and they're ar-gu-ing still!

KEEPING TIME — CONDUCTING

When someone leads a group in singing or playing a musical composition, he is called the "conductor." Have you ever watched a conductor at a concert or on the screen? The conductor has two chief functions: he must start the music (attack) and keep the performers together throughout the composition; he must also guide them in expressing the mood and meaning of the work (interpretation). These functions are done by motions of the arms (beating time) and by facial expression. The eyes of the conductor are his chief means of guiding the performers.

In beating time it is customary to employ certain movements which are understood by all musicians. The conductor should practice these movements until they become automatic; he then can concentrate on interpretation.

The beats in two-part measure are: I. down, 2. up. The beats in three-part measure are: I. down, 2. out (right), 3. up. The little dotted line indicates a preparatory movement, to warn the performers and give them a chance to take breath. When a composition begins on an up-beat, the conductor begins his preparatory motion at the location of the previous beat.

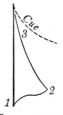

Two-part measure

Three-part measure

Every student should learn at least the elements of conducting. In the earlier grades you have learned to keep time by means of strokes, either straight up and down, or more gracefully, by curved movements. Now you can keep time both for yourself or in leading others by using the universally accepted movements. When reading music your motions should be small and quiet, but when conducting others they should be distinct and positive. Not only is it an excellent thing for each student to lead the class from time to time, but the listening lessons can be made increasingly interesting and valuable by pretending to be the conductor and directing as you listen.

Dear Land of All My Love

SIDNEY LANIER

WILLIAM G. HAMMOND

Long as thine art shall love true love,_ Long as thy sci-ence truth shall know,

Long as thine ea-gle harms no dove, Long as law by____ law shall grow,

Long as thy God is God a-bove, Thy broth-er ev-'ry man be-low,

So long, dear land of all my love, Thy name shall shine, thy fame shall grow.

The Festival

C. KLINGEMANN

FELIX MENDELSSOHN-BARTHOLDY

1. Mu-sic is scat-tered through the air, The dis-tant bells are ring - ing,
2. All to the fes - ti - val are gone, With hopes of pleas-ure beam - ing,
3. Hark to the pipe, a brid - al train Is slow - ly pass-ing yon - der,

Scarce-ly the winds to whis-per dare, The birds are sweet - ly sing - ing,
Here in this house I'm left a-lone, To lose my-self__ in dream - ing,
Seek-ing the church, and now a-gain Up - on my grief__ I pon - der,

The birds are sweet-ly sing-ing.   The or-gan's note, the cho-ral song,
To lose my-self_ in dream-ing.   They rev-el there with laugh and jest,
Up-on my grief_ I pon-der.   For I am ver-y lone-ly here,

Float sol-emn-ly the vale__ a-long,_____   Float sol-emn-ly the
While I am with my grief__op-pressed,_____   While I am with my
For I am lone - ly here!_____   While one there is if

1.
vale_____ a - long.
grief_____ op -
he_____ were

2.
pressed.   Hark!

3.
near! While one__ there is if he_____ were near!

Songs Great Artists Sing. At no time in his life is the unchanged soprano voice of a boy more beautiful than at the sixth or seventh grade level. Girls' voices, too, are often particularly lovely at this age. It is a time when special attention may be given to singing with fine tone quality, distinct pronunciation of the words, and expressive inter-pretation. These are the skills which all great singers strive to cultivate.

Apple Time

MARTHA DABNEY

FOLK SONG from YUGOSLAVIA

Ap - ple time, the ap-ples hang thick, Ap - ple time, and
Ap - ple time, the ap-ples hang red, As I climb they're

plen - ty to pick. 'Neath the tree a song is ring-ing,
o - ver my head. Down be - low the song is call-ing,

Sue is in the or-chard sing-ing. Sing on, Sue,
Look up, Sue, an ap-ple's fall - ing, Picked for you,

I love you! Sing on, Sue, I love_you!
charm - ing Sue, Picked for you, charm - ing_Sue!

Dance!
(Five-part Round)

Adapted from the original by
ELIZABETH BENNETT

OLD SWEDISH

Dance all you choose, Don't mind a - bout your shoes! If

these wear out I'll buy you new ones, Buy you all that

you can use. Dance all you choose!

Let All Be Joyful

(Canon)

CYNTHIA STEWART   LUDWIG VAN BEETHOVEN

Let all be joy - ful, Joy - - - ful; Join_

_____ us in sing - ing, Our glad voic - es ring - ing!

Come, My Soul

F. R. L. CANITZ   FRANZ JOSEPH HAYDN

1. Come, my____ soul,____ thou must be wak - ing! Now is
2. Pray that____ He____ may pros - per ev - er Each en-
3. Think that____ He____ thy ways be - hold - eth; He un-
4. On - ly____ God's____ free gifts a - buse not, Light re-

break - ing O'er the earth____ an - oth - er day;____
deav - or, When thine aim____ is good____ and true;____
fold - eth Ev - 'ry fault____ that lurks____ with - in;____
fuse not, But His spir - it's voice____ o - bey;____

Come to____ Him____ Who made this splen - dor, See thou
But that____ He____ may ev - er thwart thee, And con-
He the____ hid - den shame glossed o - ver Can dis-
Thou with____ Him____ shalt dwell, be - hold - ing Light en-

ren - der All thy fee - ble strength____ can pay.
vert thee, When thou e - vil wouldst____ pur - sue.
cov - er, And dis - cern____ each deed____ of sin.
fold - ing All things in____ un - cloud - ed day.

This melody is the principal theme of the First Movement of Haydn's Symphony No. 93 in D Major.

Botany Bay

Oh! there's Glas-gow and Ber-wick and Pen-ter-ville,_____ There's
It's not leav-ing old Eng-land we care a-bout,_____ Nor

Ports-mouth and old__ Dart-moor;_____ But__ they ain't of in-t'rest to
sail-ing for shores far a-way,_____ It's the bloom-ing mo-not-o-ny

none of us,_____ For we're bound for a far for-eign shore._____
wears us out,_____ And the pros-pect of Bot-a-ny Bay._____

CHORUS

Sing-ing too-roo-lee oo-roo-lee oo-roo-lay_____ (Also)*

Too-roo-lee oo-roo-lee-ay__(Likewise)* too-roo-lee oo-roo-lee

* (The italicized words are to be spoken)   8

oo - roo - lay_____ *(Not for-getting)* * Too - roo - lee oo - roo - lee - ay._____

Chording

In the Fifth Book of NEW MUSIC HORIZONS you were told how to play accompaniments on the piano by "chording". There are a great many songs that can be accompanied by a few simple chords. BOTANY BAY requires only three chords, the C, F, and G_7 chords. These chords are shown below. After you have found these chords on the piano, you can sing the song and accompany yourself or others by playing the chords as marked above the notes.

The C chord is made of the tones C-E-G.
The F chord is made of the tones F-A-C.
The G_7 chord is made of the tones G-B-D-F. Sometimes B or D is omitted.
The tones of any chord may be arranged in different orders.

The following chords are needed to accompany BOTANY BAY.

The relationship of the Treble and Bass Staves

Bass Middle Treble

"The relationship of the Treble and Bass Staves" is shown above on the Great Staff of eleven lines. It is difficult to recognize the location of notes on so many lines and therefore musicians have decided to use a staff of five lines. When high notes are to be sung or played, the upper part of the Great Staff is used. These five lines are called the Treble Staff and are indicated by the G Clef (𝄞). When low notes are to be performed, the lower part of the Great Staff is used. This is called the Bass Staff and is indicated by the F Clef (𝄢).

A number of songs in this book, the Sixth Book of NEW MUSIC HORIZONS, are marked for chording. If you are in doubt about the chords in different keys, turn to page 224, where you will find the basic chords in ten different keys. Some additional useful chords are also given. Suggestions for playing accompaniments are given on page 225.

A Canon

W. Otto Miessner

W. Otto Miessner

Come and lend your voice to a can - on,

Here's a song that has no end.

The Cuckoo Sounds His Call

From the German
by Nancy Byrd Turner

Old German Catch

A - wake from sleep and dream-ing; The cuck-oo calls a - way;

See, on the moun-tain gleam - ing Ap - pears the morn-ing ray.

A - wak - en, the sun is beam-ing;

The cuck - oo re - peats his call!

Cuck-oo! Cuck- oo! Cuck - oo!

Cuck - oo! Cuck - oo! Cuck - oo!

The Catch, THE CUCKOO SOUNDS HIS CALL, will test your ability to keep time. It is
  called a Catch because the rests make it necessary for the voices to come in at odd
  times, to "catch" the place.
*When the first voice reaches this point in the Canon, the second voice starts at the
  beginning.

LEONARD BACON

JOHN HATTON

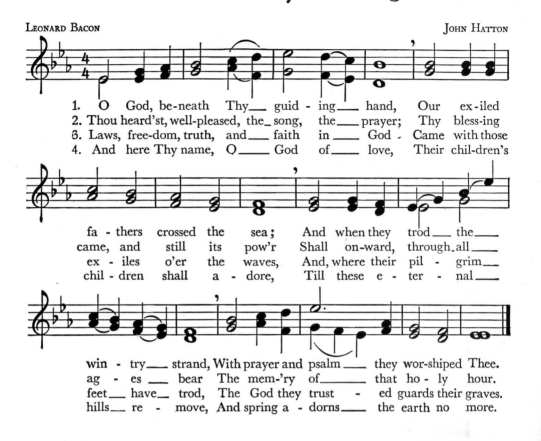

1. O God, be-neath Thy guid-ing hand, Our ex-iled
2. Thou heard'st, well-pleased, the song, the prayer; Thy bless-ing
3. Laws, free-dom, truth, and faith in God, Came with those
4. And here Thy name, O God of love, Their chil-dren's

fa-thers crossed the sea; And when they trod the
came, and still its pow'r Shall on-ward, through all
ex-iles o'er the waves, And, where their pil-grim
chil-dren shall a-dore, Till these e-ter-nal

win-try strand, With prayer and psalm they wor-shiped Thee.
ag-es bear The mem-'ry of that ho-ly hour.
feet have trod, The God they trust-ed guards their graves.
hills re-move, And spring a-dorns the earth no more.

KEEPING TIME — CONDUCTING

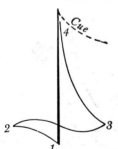

Four-part measure

In conducting four-part measure the beats are: 1. down, 2. in (left), 3. out (right), 4. up. Each movement should be distinct, the down beat should clearly be down, and nothing else, and the other beats equally clear in their proper places. There should be no wild waving of the arms, though very slight preparatory motions are sometimes desirable so that the performers will not be caught unaware of what the conductor is about to do.

In aiming to make your conducting expressive, you will soon discover that strong passages require a strong beat, quiet passages a quiet beat, and so forth. Try to make every movement fit the nature of the music. Some people fall into this naturally, others require more practice, but everyone can learn to lead simple music.

Again let us remind you to practice conducting the familiar compositions which you hear from the phonograph or over the radio; or conduct your own singing, aloud or silent; every conductor has learned much in just this way.

Courtesy NBC

Arturo Toscanini conducting an orchestral rehearsal

Palomita

TRADITIONAL

MEXICAN FOLK TUNE
Arranged by MANUEL M. PONCE

Pa - lo - mi - ta, we'll wan - der to - geth - er_____ In the
Pa - lo - mi - ta, va - mos a mi tie - rra_____ y se-

vale where the or - ang - es grow, Lit - tle dove, in the warm sum - mer
re - mos fe - li - ces los dos. Go - za - re - mos lo que un al - ma en

weath - er_____ We shall noth - ing but hap - pi - ness know;_____ There the
cie - rra_____ y es - ta - re - mos en gra - cia de Dios;_____ ¿Por qué

heav - ens all az - ure are shin - ing And flow - ers a - bun - dant and
quie - ro de ti se - pa - rar - me? Ten - go o - tros a - mo - res, ten-

Page 13

bright are en-twin-ing;____ Pa-lo-mi-ta, we'll wan-der to-geth-er____ In the vale where the or-ang-es grow.____

go o-tros con-sue-los.____ Pa-lo-mi-ta, va-mos a mi tie-rra____ y se-re-mos fe-li-ces los dos.____

The Hunter

From the GERMAN

FOLK SONG from the RHINELAND

A hunt-er on the hill, Who gal-lops o'er the mead-ows green,
Now bring to me my horse, And help me strap my sad-dle on,

A-fol-low-ing the hounds, Sings through the air so keen;
A-gain I'll gal-lop forth, All fresh at ear-ly dawn.

"Hal-loo, hal-loo!" Full mer-ry is the hunt-er's life,

A-fol-low-ing the hounds His clear "Hal-loo" re-sounds.

We Still Are In His Keeping

(Chorale)

Virginia Harrison

Severus Gastorius 1675
Harmonized by Johann Sebastian Bach

The ways of God are won-drous ways; Most gen-tly will He guide us. Through all our nights and all our days His love will walk be-side us. His faith-ful-ness our lives will bless; If wak-ing or if sleep-ing We still are in His keep-ing.

The Ugly Duckling

From the original Spanish
by Jane Rolfe Randolph

Folk Song from Costa Rica

1. There once was an ug-ly duck-ling,_____ Shab-by of col-or and feath-er; All his play-mates called him home-ly____ When-ev-er they swam to-geth-er._____

3. Then sud-den-ly, O, what pleas-ure!_____ Chil-dren came run-ning and chuck-ling, "Look, a hand-some swan," they shout-ed____ And that was the ug-ly duck-ling!____

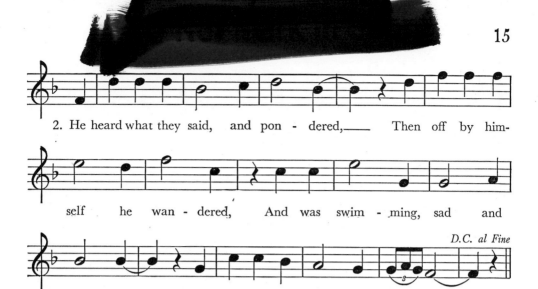

2. He heard what they said, and pon - dered,____ Then off by him-

self he wan - dered, And was swim - ming, sad and

D.C. al Fine

lone - ly____ With fish - es for com - rades on - ly.____

The triplets (♫) are to be sung with a quick little turn of the voice. This is a familiar effect in Spanish music.

The Captive

Translated from the GREEK
by ANDRONIKE MEKELATOS
Paraphrased by CYNTHIA STEWART

FOLK SONG from GREECE

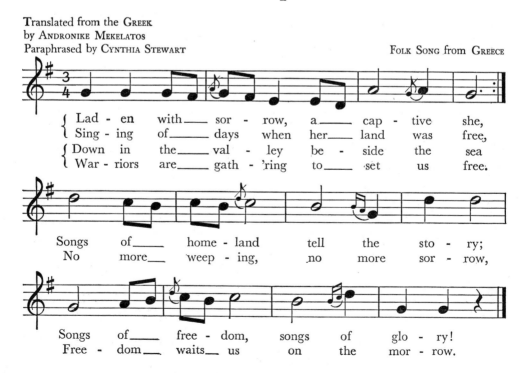

Lad - en with____ sor - row, a.____ cap - tive she,
Sing - ing of____ days when her____ land was free,
Down in the____ val - ley be - side the sea
War - riors are____ gath - 'ring to____ set us free.

Songs of____ home - land tell the sto - ry;
No more____ weep - ing, no more sor - row,

Songs of____ free - dom, songs of glo - ry!
Free - dom____ waits____ us on the mor - row.

16 A Highland Lad My Love Was Born

ROBERT BURNS   OLD SCOTTISH TUNE

1. A____ High-land lad my__ love was born, The Low-land laws__ he____
2. With his phil - a - beg and__ tar - tan plaid, And gude clay - more_doun_
3. They__ ban-ished him be - yond the sea; But ere the bud_was__

held in scorn; But he still was faith-fu'____ to his clan, My____
by his side; The____ la - dies' hearts he ____ did tre - pan, My__
on the tree A - doun my cheek_the__ pearl - ies ran, Em -

gal - lant_ braw_John _ High - land - man.
gal - lant_ braw_John__ High - land - man. Sing__ hey, my braw John
brac - ing__ my__John__ High - land - man.

High-land-man, Sing ho, my braw John High-land-man; There's_no a lad _ in __

a' the lan' Was__ match_wi'__ my__ John__ High-land - man.

The Bell Doth Toll

(Three-Part Round)   ENGLISH

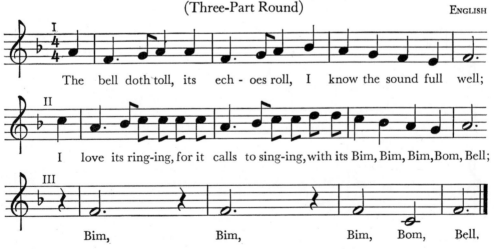

The bell doth toll, its ech - oes roll, I know the sound full well;

I love its ring-ing, for it calls to sing-ing, with its Bim, Bim, Bim, Bom, Bell;

Bim,   Bim,   Bim, Bom, Bell.

It's Autumn in the World

MARTHA DABNEY

OLD NETHERLANDS FOLK SONG

The gol-den-rod has light-ed Its can-dles, bright and clear,
The birds are mak-ing read-y To jour-ney south a-gain;

And star-ry pur-ple as-ters Are shin-ing far and near.
The rob-in and his la-dy, The swal-low and the wren.

The clouds are drift-ing feath-ers, The smoke is light-ly curled;
All yel-low, gold, and scar-let, The leaves are down-ward whirled.

White frost is on the pump-kin And Au-tumn's in the world!
The crick-et tunes his fid-dle; It's Au-tumn in the world!

17

The Lark's Song

Felix Mendelssohn-Bartholdy

O lark, gai - ly sing, And her - ald the spring, How
In sum - mer's de-light, When val - ley and height With

sweet - ly thy glad notes are ris - ing! To list to thy lay,
God's gra-cious gifts are a - bound - ing. Then, tune - ful and clear,

I has - ten a - way, The world's pet - ty tri - als de -
From far and from near, Thy song of thanks - giv - ing is

spis - ing, The world's pet - ty tri - als de - spis - ing.
sound - ing, Thy song of thanks-giv - ing is sound - ing.

At the Dance

NANCY BYRD TURNER

CZECH FOLK DANCE

She: When__ I am read-y, sir, Your__ part - ner__
He: Proud__la - dy, let me say With__ you I__

then__ I'll__ be, So__ wait a while,__ sir,
well__ a - gree, If__ I am pa - tient

Then dance with me. I've prom - ised man-y danc - es,
Part - ners we'll be. But though you find it pain - ful,

And you must__ take your chanc - es, Your__ part - ner
Oth - ers are__ less dis-dain - ful, A__ doz - en

I'll__ be When I am free.
I__ see Who'll dance with me!

Cock-a-doo-dle-doo!
(Three-part Round)

Group project in Creative Workshop
A. I. N. M., MARY JARMAN NELSON, Teacher

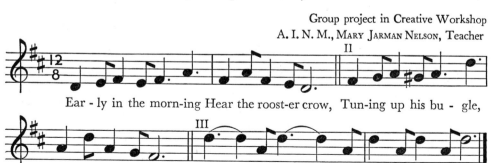

Ear - ly in the morn-ing Hear the roost-er crow, Tun-ing up his bu - gle,

Can't you hear him blow: Cock - a - doo - dle, doo-dle-doo-dle-doo!

Polka

FOLK TUNE from BOHEMIA
used for the first POLKA

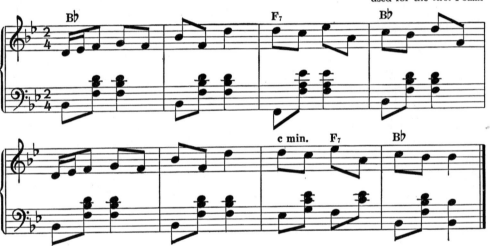

The very popular dance step, the polka, is said to have been invented by a young Bohemian peasant girl about 1830. According to the story, a noble was passing through the hall of his castle in Bohemia when he heard singing and the patter of feet. He traced the sounds to the room of one of the maid-servants. The door was partly open, and the noble looked in. The young girl was dancing and singing merrily. When she saw her master, she stopped suddenly and was very much frightened.

The noble spoke kindly to her and told her not to be afraid. He asked her where she had learned to dance that step. "Oh, I was just making up steps to the song I was singing," she replied.

"And would you teach that dance to my guests at the ball tonight?" asked the noble.

The girl was almost too happy to speak. That night she taught the noble's guests the dance she had made up.

About 1835, a Bohemian musician, Josef Neruda, introduced the music and the dance into Prague. From that city it spread quickly throughout Europe.

The word "polka" rhymes with the Czech word "holka," which means "girl."

Polka

Top of room

No. I

No. II

Bottom of room

When you dance, your footsteps form patterns on the floor. If the bottoms of your shoes were inked, they would print the patterns so that you could see them. You would then notice that some dances, like the Waltz or the Polka, repeat the step-patterns over and over without any general plan. But some other dances, like the Virginia Reel or the Minuet, form well-organized floor designs. These designs are shown below, and will give you an idea as to how you can work out on paper the designs of other dances or can invent original designs of your own. You can use the polka step, the waltz step, or any other familiar dance as your step-pattern. Your designs could be repeated as many times as you wished, and could also be alternated with contrasting designs.

The square represents a boy and the circle represents a girl. The directions in which you move may be forward, backward, sideward, and around, and diagonal. In making a new design, move in one direction until the end of the musical phrase, then change your direction. See if you can skip, waltz, or polka to the same design. Choose some music that you know and let the design (form) of the music suggest the movement and changes of direction in your floor design.

Design No. I is danced to the polka step, and is for one couple. They polka forward to 1, separate to 2, come together at 3, then go forward to 4, always changing direction at the change of musical phrases. The design may be repeated any number of times. If four couples were to dance this design in a circle, the pattern would look like No. II. Try the same design to other dance steps, such as the waltz or the schottische. Then use some other music to create a new floor design. Always try to make your steps and designs fit the spirit, rhythm, and design of the music.

Floor Design for the Virginia Reel. Observe how partners meet for bow, turn with right hand, etc. First couple slide down center and return. The reel comes next, then first couple go down back of own line to form an arch under which all other dancers pass.

Floor Design for the Minuet. The minuet can be danced by any number of couples. Watch the arrows on the design. Dancers go diagonally forward, move to the left in a semi-circle, and go down center in a straight line. Then couples go right and left alternately, circling around to leave dance floor.

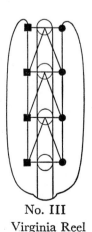

No. III

Virginia Reel

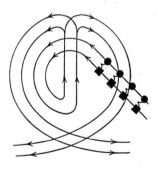

No. IV

Minuet

Song of Praise

C. H. HOHMAN

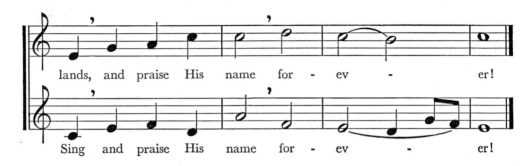

lands, and praise His name for - ev - er!

Sing and praise His name for - ev - er!

At Parting

NANCY BYRD TURNER   CZECH FOLK SONG

Now it's time for leav - ing, But in - stead of griev - ing
We'll re - mem - ber gay times, Sing - ing times and play times,

We'll be glad. Let's look back_ to_ all we've done,
Sun and rain. They are gone,_ but_ e - ven so

Let's look back_ to_
They are gone,_ but_

All the frol - ic_ and the fun That we've had.
Jol - ly days like_ those, you know, Come a - gain.

all we've done, All the frol-ic and the fun we've had.
e - ven so Jol - ly days like those will come a - gain.

SONG OF PRAISE and AT PARTING are excellent examples of two different styles of part singing. The opening measures are harmonic, with the melody in one voice part and an accompaniment in the other part. Then the songs become contrapuntal, both voice parts having melodies which are equally important. The songs close harmonically. Everyone enjoys singing Rounds and Canons, which are simple forms of contrapuntal music. Other forms will be brought to your attention as they appear later in this book.

Hymn of Praise

From FOUNDLING HOSPITAL COLLECTION, 1796   FRANZ JOSEPH HAYDN

Praise the Lord! ye heav'ns a - dore_ Him, Praise Him, an - gels
Praise the Lord! for He is glo - rious; Nev - er shall His

in the_height; Sun and moon, re -joice be - fore_Him, Praise Him, all ye
prom-ise_ fail; God hath made His saints vic-to - rious, Sin and death shall

stars of_ light. Praise the Lord!_ for He hath spo - ken,
not pre - vail. Praise the God_ of our sal - va - tion;

Worlds His might - y voice o - beyed; Laws which nev - er
Hosts on high, His power pro-claim; Heav'n and earth, and

shall be bro - ken, For their_ guid - ance_ He hath_ made.
all cre-a - tion, Laud and_ mag - ni - fy His_ name!

On one of his visits to England, Haydn was deeply impressed with the national hymn,
"God Save the King." He thought it his duty to supply Austria with a similar hymn, and,
in 1797, he wrote the Austrian Hymn to the words, "God Preserve Emperor Francis."
Later Haydn used this hymn as the slow movement of a string quartet, in the form of an
air with variations, reminding one of the variations in the second movement of his
"Surprise" Symphony.

Themes from CONTRA-DANCE No. 1
by LUDWIG VAN BEETHOVEN (1770-1827)

Starting with your beginning music books, NEW MUSIC HORIZONS has aimed to help you recognize the form, or structure, of the music you were singing and hearing. Your earliest songs, learned by rote, were taught by phrases, and your attention was called to similar and different phrases. You were asked to notice how some phrases were repeated, while others were different for contrast, thus making various structural designs. By using letters you could indicate how these designs were built: A A B A, or A B A C, etc. Then, in the Fifth Book, you were shown how these little four-phrase songs could be taken as larger units, and by repetition and contrast could form longer songs. You also noticed how, by means of verses and choruses, songs could be lengthened and varied. The four-phrase unit was called a Period, and we used Roman numerals to show the organization of these Periods: I II I, or I I II I, etc. Then we listened to some short instrumental selections and to dance music, and discovered that the same general principles of design that were found in songs applied also to instrumental forms.

There are many good reasons why some acquaintance with simple musical forms is desirable. In the first place, it will enable you to "keep the place" as you listen to a piece of music, to know what to expect, and to experience the pleasure of being ready for a repetition of an earlier theme when it is due to return. We all find pleasure in recognizing a familiar theme or melody; a knowledge of form increases that pleasure by adding the fun of anticipating the return of the themes in a piece of music. We can follow the composer's thought when he introduces contrasting themes or makes novel and unexpected changes in the usual patterns.

An excellent little selection for listening to Period repetitions and contrasts is Beethoven's "Contra-Dance," No. 1. Some of the themes are given above. See if you can recognize each of these themes as it occurs and is repeated, and can indicate the form of the complete dance by numerals: I, II, etc. Some pieces have little interludes or closing codas; you must watch for them. There are many other short instrumental pieces which you will enjoy studying in the same way, particularly marches and dances. But any good piece of music will serve, and in a short while you will find your listening enjoyment greatly increased by your study of music form.

Down in the Valley

From "The Singin' Gatherin'"

Folk Song from the
Kentucky Mountains

*Three slow beats in a measure, each
beat the value of a dotted quarter note.*

(Humming, breathe at different times to maintain sustained tone.)

1. Down in the val-ley, the val-ley so low, Hang your head
love me, love whom you please, Throw your arms
round me, be-fore it's too late, Throw your arms
love me, none else will do, My heart is
let-ter, con-tain-ing three lines, An-swer my

o - ver, hear the winds blow. Hear the winds blow, dear, hear the winds
round me, give my heart ease. Give my heart ease, dear, give my heart
round me, feel my heart break. Feel my heart break, dear, feel my heart
break-ing, dear, just for you. Break-ing for you, dear, break-ing for
ques-tion: Will you be mine? Will you be mine, dear, will you be

blow, Hang your head o - ver, hear the winds blow. 2. If you don't
ease, Throw your arms round me, Give my heart ease. 3. Throw your arms
break, Throw your arms round me, feel my heart break. 4. If you don't
you, My heart is break-ing, dear, just for you. 5. Writ-ing this
mine, An-swer my ques-tion: Will you be   mine?

Chording by voices is not unlike piano chording, and it can often be indicated by similar chord markings. Practice in singing chording exercises will make you familiar with
the effect of these chords. It will also give you experience in tone blending, so
helpful in expressive three-part singing.

Gum Tree Canoe

TRADITIONAL

AMERICAN FOLK SONG

1. On Tom - big - bee riv - er, so bright, I was born,
2. All day in the field the soft cot - ton I hoe,
3. With my hands on the ban - jo and toe on the oar,
4. One night the stream bore us so far, far a way,

In a hut made of husks of the tall yel - low corn,
I___ think of my Jul - ia and sing as I go.
I'll___ sing to the sound of the riv - er's soft roar.
That we could - n't come back, so we thought we'd just stay.

And there I first met with my Jul - ia so true,
Oh, I'll catch her a bird with a wing of true blue,
While stars they look down on my Jul - ia so true,
We spied a tall ship with a flag of true blue,

And I rowed her a - bout in my gum tree can - oe.
And at night sail her round in my gum tree can - oe.
And___ dance in her eyes in my gum tree can - oe.
And it took us in tow with my gum tree can - oe.

CHORUS   B♭   F

Sing-ing, row a - way, row, o'er the wa - ters so blue,

C   F   C₇   F

Like a feath - er we'll float in my gum tree can - oe.

Columbus

MARY BUDLONG

JACOB WEINBERG

A phan-tom land lay beck-on-ing Long leagues be-yond the

shore-less sea, No friend-ly stars for reck-on-ing, Un-swerv-ing, daunt-less

heart had he.__ He searched the shad-ows of the dark And

held the pi-lot to his will; The cry that on-ward sped his bark

Down through the years, un-dy-ing, ech-oes still: "Sail on! Sail on!"____

English Traditional   Irish Air

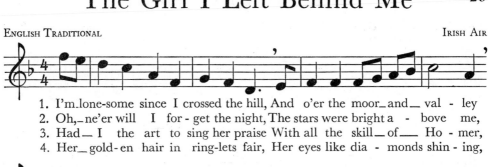

1. I'm lone-some since I crossed the hill, And o'er the moor and val - ley
2. Oh, ne'er will I for - get the night, The stars were bright a - bove me,
3. Had I the art to sing her praise With all the skill of Ho - mer,
4. Her gold-en hair in ring-lets fair, Her eyes like dia - monds shin - ing,

Such heav-y thoughts my heart do fill, Since part-ing with my Sal - ly;
And gen-tly lent their sil-v'ry light, When first she vowed to love me.
One on-ly theme should fill my lays, The charms of my own true lov - er.
Her slen-der waist with car-riage chaste May leave the swain re - pin - ing.

I seek no more the fine and gay, For each does but re - mind me
But now I'm bound to Bright-on Camp; Kind Heav'n, may fa-vor find me,
So let the night be e'er so dark Or e'er so wet and wind - y,
Ye gods a-bove, oh hear my prayer To my beau-teous fair to bind me,

How swift the hours did pass a-way With the girl I left be - hind me.
And send me safe - ly back a-gain To the girl I left be - hind me.
Kind Heav-en, send me back a-gain To the girl I left be - hind me.
And send me safe - ly back a-gain To the girl I left be - hind me.

5. The bee shall honey taste no more,
   The dove become a ranger,
   The falling waves shall cease to roar,
   Ere I shall seek to change her.
   The vows we registered above
   Shall ever cheer and bind me,
   In constancy to her I love,
   The girl I left behind me.

6. My mind her form shall still retain
   In sleeping or in waking,
   Until I see my love again,
   For whom my heart is breaking.
   If ever I return that way
   And she should not decline me,
   I evermore will live and stay
   With the girl I left behind me.

THE GIRL I LEFT BEHIND ME is one of the best known of all marching songs. It is especially useful for fife and drum corps. Among the pupils who play the drum, some will be interested to arrange drum parts for snare and bass drums. Where there are no fifes or flutes, the melody may be whistled to imitate these instruments.

I Thank My God

Paraphrased from the GERMAN
by NANCY BYRD TURNER

JOHANN SEBASTIAN BACH

The Lord's strong hand will hold Wher-ev-er___ I___ may___ be, That
What-ev-er___ is my___ share, With that I'll___ do___ my___ best, And

prom-ise bright-er shines than gold, And all is___ well with___ me. There-
see the sun-shine ev-'ry-where, And leave to___Him the___ rest. His

fore I trust my God, And stand and take my part, Con-
word my guide will prove, My help on ev - 'ry road; I

tent-ed all a - long life's road, And hap-py___ in___ my___ heart.
shall not lack for light or love, There-fore I___ thank___ my___ God.

SHARP CHROMATICS

Half-Step Scale, Sharps

Sharp-4 in the Key of C

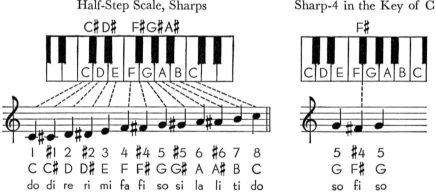

1	#1	2	#2	3	4	#4	5	#5	6	#6	7	8
C	C#	D	D#	E	F	F#	G	G#	A	A#	B	C
do	di	re	ri	mi	fa	fi	so	si	la	li	ti	do

5	#4	5
G	F#	G
so	fi	so

The diagram, "The Half-Step Scale, Sharps," will show where C#, D#, F#, G#, and
A# may be found on the piano keyboard and on the staff. Look through the song,
I THANK MY GOD, and see how many times you can find a sharp chromatic.

By referring to the diagram, "Sharp-4 in the Key of C," you will find that the sharp
chromatic in measures six and seven is called sharp-four (#4), F-sharp (F#), or by the
syllable **fi**. Sing and play the little three-tone exercise, 5 - #4 - 5 (**so - fi - so**), which
is a study in half-steps, and sounds like 8 - 7 - 8 (**do - ti - do**).

In measure eleven you will find another sharp chromatic, called sharp-five (#5), G-sharp
(G#), or **si**. You can find G-sharp on the piano keyboard, and can make up your own
three-tone exercise: A - G# - A, 6 - #5 - 6, **la - si - la**.

Brotherhood

Rev. Frank Mason North

Ludwig van Beethoven

Where cross the crowd - ed ways___ of life, Where sound the
Till sons of men shall learn___ Thy love, And fol - low

cries of race___ and clan, A - bove the noise___ of
where Thy feet___ have trod; Till glo - rious from___ Thy

self - ish strife___ We hear Thy voice,___ O Son___ of Man.
heav'n a - bove___ Shall come the cit - y of___ our God.

Mazurka

Marion Bergman

Czech Folk Song

Four red ap - ples grand-ma had, and grand-pa had but two.___
What a bright red coat you're wear-ing to our dance so gay;___

"Grand-ma, give me one of yours, and then we'll each have three."___
The ma-zur - ka we are step-ping, hap-py all the day.___

Chorus

Tra la la, la la la la la, Tra la la, la la la la la.

"Grand-ma, give me one of yours, and then we'll each have three."___
The ma-zur - ka we are step - ping, hap-py all the day.___

The Last Rose of Summer

Thomas Moore

Old Irish Melody
(Version by Sir Charles Villiers Stanford)

1. 'Tis the last rose___ of____ sum-mer Left___ bloom-ing___ a -
2. I'll not leave thee,___ thou___ lone one, To____ pine on___ the____
3. So___ soon may___ I____ fol-low, When__ friend-ships_ de -

lone; All her love - ly____ com - pan - ions Are____
stem; Since the love - ly____ are____ sleep - ing, Go,____
cay, And from love's shin - ing____ cir - cle The____

fad - ed___ and____ gone; No____ flow'r of____ her____
sleep thou__ with____ them. Thus___ kind - ly____ I____
gems drop__ a - way! When__ true hearts_ lie____

kin - dred, No____ rose - bud__ is____ nigh,____ To re-
scat - ter Thy___ leaves o'er__ the____ bed,____ Where thy
with-ered, And___ fond ones__ are____ flown,____ Oh,____

flect back__ her____ blush - es And___ give sigh__ for____ sigh.
mates of____ the____ gar - den Lie____ scent - less___ and___ dead.
who would_ in - hab - it This__ bleak world_ a - lone?

Songs Great Artists Sing. The old Irish folk song, THE LAST ROSE OF SUMMER, was made world famous by the composer Friedrich von Flotow, who included it in his opera, "Martha." The opera was long a favorite of the greatest sopranos, who made this melody one of the climaxes of the work. You, too, should try to bring out all the beauty of this song.

Vocal Chording

Eb   Ab   Eb   Bb7   Eb   C min.   G7   C min.   Bb7   Eb

All in a Garden Green

TRADITIONAL   ENGLISH FOLK SONG

All in a gar-den green Two lov-ers sat at ease, As
Quoth he,"Most love-ly maid, My troth shall aye en-dure; And

they could scarce be seen A-mong, a-mong the leaf-y trees.
be not thou a-fraid, But rest thee, rest thee, still se-cure."

They long had loved y-fore, And no long-er than tru-ly,
She heard with joy the youth That he would love her long,

In that time of the year, In that time
So she trust-ed in his truth, So she trust-ed

of the year Com-eth 'twixt May and Ju-ly.
in his truth And lis-tened to his song.

In Elizabethan times July was pronounced to rhyme with "truly."

A Free Spirit

Paraphrased from the original by
ELIZABETH BENNETT

FOLK SONG from ALSACE

The two accompanying parts may be played by
instruments or hummed by selected voices.

1. { My thoughts are as____ free as wind o'er the o - cean
   { And no one can____ see their form or their mo - tion.

2. { A glim - mer - ing____ fire the dark - ness will bright-en;
   { My soar - ing de - sire all trou - bles can light - en.

3. { My wish and de - sire for Free - dom are call - ing;
   { From Lib - er - ty's____ fire the sparks now are fall - ing.

No hunt - er can find them, No trap ev - er bind them;
Though pris - on en - fold me Its walls can - not hold me,
The bright flames a - glow - ing A path - way are show - ing

My lips may be____ still, but I think_what I will.
No cap - tive I'll____ be while my spir - it is free!
To lands that will____ be, where all man - kind is free.

America, the Beautiful

Katherine Lee Bates

Samuel A. Ward

1. O beau-ti-ful for spa-cious skies, For am-ber waves of grain,
2. O beau-ti-ful for pil-grim feet, Whose stern, im-pas-sioned stress
3. O beau-ti-ful for he-roes proved In lib-er-at-ing strife,
4. O beau-ti-ful for pa-triot dream That sees be-yond the years

For pur-ple moun-tain maj-es-ties A-bove the fruit-ed plain!
A thor-ough-fare for free-dom beat A-cross the wil-der-ness!
Who more than self their coun-try loved, And mer-cy more than life!
Thine al-a-bas-ter cit-ies gleam Un-dimmed by hu-man tears!

A-mer-i-ca! A-mer-i-ca! God shed His grace on thee,_____
A-mer-i-ca! A-mer-i-ca! God mend thine ev-'ry flaw,_____
A-mer-i-ca! A-mer-i-ca! May God thy gold re-fine,_____
A-mer-i-ca! A-mer-i-ca! God shed His grace on thee,_____

And crown thy good with broth-er-hood From sea to shin-ing sea!
Con-firm thy soul in self-con-trol, Thy lib-er-ty in law!
Till all suc-cess be no-ble-ness, And ev-'ry gain di-vine!
And crown thy good with broth-er-hood From sea to shin-ing sea!

Vocal Chording

C   F   G₇   C

Observe that the third voice-part starts with the same melody as the one sung by the first
voice-part at the beginning of the song.

The Maple Leaf Forever

(Canadian Patriotic Song)

ALEXANDER MUIR   ALEXANDER MUIR

1. In days of yore, from Brit-ain's shore, Wolfe the daunt-less he - ro came,
2. On man - y hard fought bat-tle fields Our brave fa-thers side by side,
3. On mer - ry Eng-land's far-famed land May kind Heav-en sweet -ly smile;

And plant-ed firm Bri-tan-nia's flag On ___ Can-a-da's fair___ do-main;
For free-dom, homes, and loved ones dear, Firm-ly stood and no - bly died;
God bless old Scot-land ev - er-more, And___ Ire - land's Em - 'rald isle!

Here may it wave, our boast and pride, And joined in love to - geth-er,
And those dear rights which they main-tained, We swear to yield them nev-er!
Then swell the song, both loud and long, Till rocks and for - est quiv-er,

The Lil - y, This-tle, Sham-rock, Rose, And Ma-ple Leaf for - ev-er!
Our watch-word ev - er - more shall be, The Ma-ple Leaf for - ev-er!
God save our King, and Heav-en bless The Ma-ple Leaf for - ev-er!

CHORUS

The Ma-ple Leaf, our em-blem dear, The Ma-ple Leaf for - ev-er!

God save our King, and Heav-en bless The Ma-ple Leaf for - ev-er!

Autumn

ELEANOR ALLETTA CHAFFEE

FOLK SONG from the UKRAINE
arranged by N. LEONTOVYCH

Last night, like a wild thing, Au-tumn danced with a step so
Hark now to the north wind, To the drums and the tem-pest

light - ly, That the sound On the leaf - y ground Seemed a
call - ing. Now the green Of the A - pril scene In a

sil - ver chime rung bright - ly; That the sound On the
gold - en show'r is fall - ing; Now the green Of the

leaf - y ground Seemed a sil - ver chime rung bright - ly.
A - pril scene In a gold-en show'r is fall - ing.

Mother's Advice

From the ITALIAN by
ELIZABETH BENNETT

ITALIAN FOLK SONG

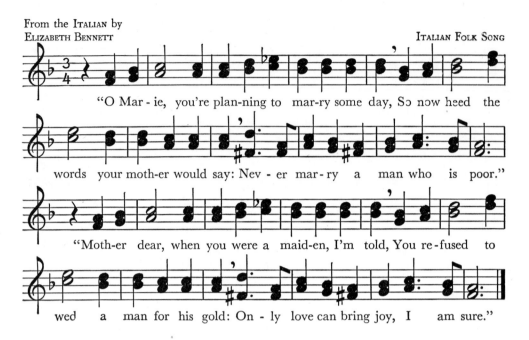

"O Mar - ie, you're plan-ning to mar-ry some day, So now heed the

words your moth-er would say: Nev - er mar-ry a man who is poor."

"Moth-er dear, when you were a maid-en, I'm told, You re-fused to

wed a man for his gold: On - ly love can bring joy, I am sure."

FLAT CHROMATICS

The Half-Step Scale, Flats

Flat-7 in the Key of F

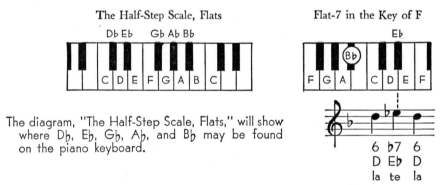

The diagram, "The Half-Step Scale, Flats," will show where Db, Eb, Gb, Ab, and Bb may be found on the piano keyboard.

6 b7 6
D Eb D
la te la

"The Half-Step Scale, Flats," may best be pictured as a descending scale, and may be played that way on the piano and bells:

C	B	Bb	A	Ab	G	Gb	F	E	Eb	D	Db	C
8	7	b7	6	b6	5	b5	4	3	b3	2	b2	1
do	ti	te	la	le	so	se	fa	mi	me	re	ra	do

By referring to the diagram, "Flat-7 in the Key of F," you will find that the flat chromatic in measures three and fifteen of Mother's Advice is called flat-seven, (b7), E-flat (Eb), or by the syllable **te**, pronounced **tay**. Sing and play the little three-tone exercise, 6 – b7 – 6 (la – te – la), which is a study in half-steps, and sounds like 3 – 4 – 3 (mi – fa – mi).

Hear Us, Father, As We Pray

JANE ROLFE RANDOLPH

WOLFGANG AMADEUS MOZART

Fa-ther, we have come be-fore Thee, Bring-ing to Thy feet a prayer.
Next, we pray for cour-age, Fa-ther; Make us brave and keep us strong,

First, we ask that love may lead us, Day and night and ev-'ry-where.
Fear-less by Thy strength to con-quer In the fight with ev-'ry wrong.

For with love be-fore us go-ing, We shall shine, our-selves, and make
And for qui-et hearts we're ask-ing, Gen-tle hearts a-long life's way;

Light a-round us on the jour-ney, Light to shine for oth-ers' sake.
Give us love and peace and cour-age; Hear us, Fa-ther, as we pray.

Vocal Chording

Walking Song

From the original FINNISH by
ELIZABETH BENNETT

CHILDREN's SONG from FINLAND
by LEEVI MADETOJA

Away Now Joyful Riding

TRADITIONAL

FR. KÜCKEN

A - way now joy-ful rid - ing, With heart and hope so light,
The trees were past us fly - ing, The moun-tains seemed to race;

My foam-ing steed now chid - ing, Then cheer-ing his quick flight.
My heart a-lone seemed dy - ing, All mocked our wea-ry pace.

Now, urge thee still more fleet! We'll have a mile most sweet.
How slow the long hours glide; The road is free and wide,

Trot, trot, trot, trot, my friend-ly steed, 'Tis love and home to meet;
Trot, trot, trot, trot, a - way, a-way! We must more fleet-ly ride;

Trot, trot, trot, trot, my friend-ly steed, 'Tis love and home to meet.
Trot, trot, trot, trot, a - way, a-way! We must more fleet-ly ride.

41

Prayer

M. LOUISE BAUM

HANS GEORG NAEGELI

Not too slowly

1. Lord, I pray Thee, Hear my ear-nest prayer.
2. Leave me nev - er, Thou who lov - est me!
3. Show, ah, show me, God of love and light,

Teach me to o - bey Thee; Make__ my path-way fair.
Guard and guide me ev - er; Keep__ me close to Thee.
How my heart may know Thee; Live__ as in Thy sight.

Lazy Laddie

(Dialogue Song)

ELEANOR ALLETTA CHAFFEE

FOLK SONG from the UKRAINE
ARRANGED by N. LEONTOVYCH

1. Lad - die, lad - die, time for mow - ing,
2. Lad - die, lad - die, are you shirk - ing?
3. Lad - die, lad - die, help your moth - er,

While you sleep the grass is grow - ing. But I feel so
Is not this your time for work - ing? But it's ear - ly,
Din - ner's on for you and broth - er. I have on - ly

snug and warm,— One more day will do no harm.
on - ly four,— Lat - er on I'll do my chore.
time to eat,— For I'm tired from head to feet.

Music in Nature

ELIZABETH BENNETT

KARL FEYE
SWEDISH COMPOSER

1. In the woods are— songs of— glad - ness, All the
2. Do you hear a— dis - tant— drum - mer And a
3. Lul - la - by, the— song of— O - cean, Oh, her

brook - lets sing in— rhyme, While the birds trill mer - ry—
wild and sweet re - frain? 'Tis the thun - der-drum of—
voice is calm and— deep. And the waves with cease - less—

mad - ness And the toss - ing trees keep time.
Sum - mer And the mu - sic of the rain.
mo - tion Lull the wea - ry world to sleep.

The Irish Washerwoman

OLD AMERICAN FIDDLE TUNE

Formation: Three couples, Virginia Reel formation.

I. Four steps forward (toward partners) and four steps back. All swing partners half way around to change places (8 counts). Forward and back again; all swing partners to original places.

II. First couple walk down the center and back. They then cast off and go to bottom while other two couples Grand Right and Left once around. The whole dance is repeated with a new first couple.

PLAYING THE STRING BASS

You are acquainted with the violin and the cello, both of which are stringed instruments played with a bow. Another member of the family of stringed instruments is the string bass, bass viol, or double bass.

It is interesting to know that in addition to being very much larger, the shape of most string basses is somewhat different from that of the violin and cello. For instance, the back of the instrument is usually flat instead of curved. It is the present-day example of the "viol" family, which was the olden forerunner of the violins of today.

The string bass is played by drawing the bow with the right hand across one of the four strings. The fingers of the left hand press the strings down on the fingerboard to make higher tones on each string. Another kind of sound is made by plucking the strings with the fingers. This is called *pizzicato*

The string bass plays the lowest notes in the music like the bass singers in a choir. The instrument is not often found in elementary school orchestras; it is too large and unwieldy for small people. But it is in all high school and concert orchestras.

You will be glad to see the instrument, to notice how the player holds it, and to hear its deep, rich tones.

TUNING THE STRING BASS

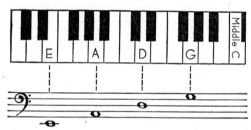

The tones produced on the string bass sound an octave lower than written.

Themes from the "Unfinished" Symphony in B minor

FRANZ SCHUBERT

The Minuet: A Dream of Long Ago

ELIZABETH BENNETT

GLUCK

{ In state - ly min - u - et my la - dy danc - es;
{ Grace - ful her move-ments are, mod - est her glanc - es.
{ While the mu - si - cians play mel - o - dies ten - der,
{ Fine court - ly gen - tle-men, la - dies so slen - der

Turn - ing to right and left, while part - ners bow, part-ners bow,—
Dance in a ball- room where can - dle lights gleam, can-dles gleam,—

Shy - ly she nods her head and curt - seys __ now.
Ghosts of the long a - go, naught but __ a __ dream.

The Wheels of Time

ELEANOR ALLETTA CHAFFEE

FRANZ ABT

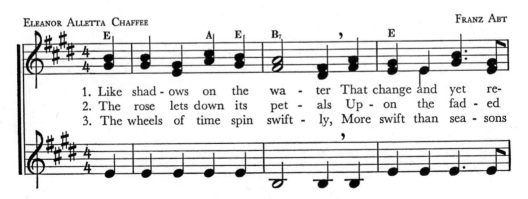

1. Like shad - ows on the wa - ter That change and yet re-
2. The rose lets down its pet - als Up - on the fad - ed
3. The wheels of time spin swift - ly, More swift than sea - sons

main,   Life   pass - es like the danc - ing Of
grass,   And   those   who loved its plant - ing All
run,   And   life seems but the mo - ment That

slant-ing sil - ver rain,   Of__ slant-ing sil - ver rain.
un - re - mem-bered pass,   All__ un - re - mem-bered pass.
lasts from sun   to   sun,   That_ lasts from sun   to   sun.

High and Blue Our Mountains Stand

JANE ROLFE RANDOLPH   FOLK SONG from SERBIA

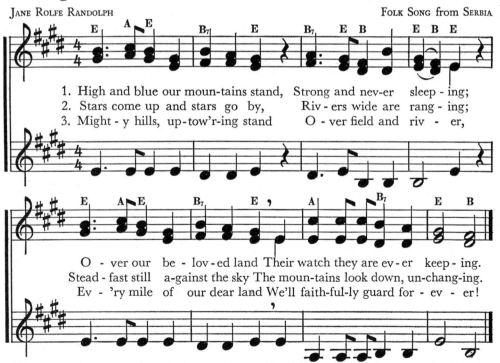

1. High and blue our moun-tains stand, Strong and nev-er   sleep-ing;
2. Stars come up and stars go by,   Riv - ers wide are rang - ing;
3. Might - y hills, up-tow'r-ing stand   O - ver field and riv - er,

O - ver our be - lov-ed land Their watch they are ev - er keep - ing.
Stead - fast still a-gainst the sky The moun-tains look down, un-chang-ing.
Ev - 'ry mile of our dear land We'll faith-ful-ly guard for - ev - er!

The unusual ending is a characteristic Serbian effect.

BROADCASTING YOUR OWN PROGRAM

Have you thought of how much fun it would be to prepare a radio program, rehearse it, and then broadcast it in your own room just as though it were going out over the air from a real station? W or K is used as the first letter for all radio stations in the United States; W for most stations east of the Mississippi River, and K for the western stations. You could use one of these letters and add the first three letters of the name of your school.

Besides the members of the class who sing or play, it will be necessary to have an announcer and a reader for the script. If you listen to your local radio stations, you can find out just how these people take part. Committees might be appointed to have charge of various details as follows: 1. Research Committee, to suggest the topic of the broadcast subject to class approval, and find information to be used by the Script Committee; 2. Music Committee, to select music material suitable to the topic; 3. Script Committee, to prepare a properly organized and timed script; 4. Production Committee, to be responsible for studio equipment, including sound effects, to select and rehearse the performers, and in general, to see that the production goes smoothly.

In writing your radio script, you must decide first on the central theme or idea. In this program we have called it "World Brotherhood." Next, you will choose your songs and instrumental numbers and then write paragraphs that will introduce the subject of the broadcast, the musical numbers, and the performers. Some selections can be done by one, two, or three of the boys and girls, and others by the whole class.

Make a microphone of your own. One can be easily imagined by using the oblong box that comes around an electric light bulb, or you can make one out of heavy paper, using the pictures for a model.

When the class sings, the pupils do not come to the microphone. Individuals or small groups stand closer as shown in the accompanying pictures.

Certain words are used in broadcasting, and we should know their meaning. "Script" is the name given to the written program which contains all the spoken words and the places for music and other sounds which are to be used. "Cue" is the signal to be given a performer when some new part of the program is to start; the teacher may point as a cue to the individual or group when the time comes to begin. Sound effects are an important part of most broadcasts. You can think of many ways of using sounds to make the program more effective. "Fade" means to become softer. "Fade under" means to continue very softly while words are being spoken. "Fade out" means to grow softer and softer until the sound stops entirely. Timing is very important. Every musical selection must be timed exactly, and the complete script with all of the music must be timed. If the song lasts for two minutes and twenty seconds, it is marked like this: 2:20. "Theme" may mean the general subject of the program, or it may mean the musical tune. If the musical selection is used to open and close the program it is called "theme music."

WORLD BROTHERHOOD

The events of recent years have made us realize that the world is, after all, not so very large. New means of transportation and communication bring us so close to the other side of the world that we can go anywhere in a very few days. Radio and telephone connect the continents and we hear voices as if they were in the next room.

Possibly you know someone who now travels overseas on business, or someone who lives in a distant country. Most of us have relatives and friends who were serving in the Armed Forces in Europe or Asia in the last war. They made many friends among different peoples. We are beginning to realize more fully the need for better understanding among all peoples so that there shall be no more war. We must learn each other's customs, each other's songs, each other's ideals, so that through understanding we may achieve world peace. The United Nations have formed an organization based on a belief in democratic ideals and world brotherhood. So, as one example of the kinds of radio programs you may wish to write, we have chosen the topic, "World Brotherhood," presenting music from some of those other countries with whom we wish to be friends.

A RADIO PROGRAM

Chimes: Do mi so $\overline{do}$
Music (Cue):   Hum BROTHERHOOD.
Music fade under and out on cue.
Announcer (Cue): World Brotherhood! Today our Sixth Grade Class is broadcasting a program of music from different countries to show how lovely their music is and to show our interest in the people of all nations. Our class, under the direction of Miss _____, our teacher, will sing the song expressing the theme — BROTHERHOOD, by Ludwig van Beethoven.
Music: BROTHERHOOD, sung by class.
Announcer: Now let us hear some of the music that comes from our friends in other countries.

*   *   *   *   *

Note: From here on, let the Announcer read a few words about the country, the composer, or the subject of the song or instrumental number, then give the title and composer, and finally, the name or names of the performers, if less than four. Otherwise, say "Sixth Grade Class" or "Vocal Group" or "Instrumental Ensemble" or "Players."

When closing your program it would be interesting to do this:

Music: Hum BROTHERHOOD. Fade under on cue but continue softly.

50

Announcer:	(Cue) And now we are at the end of this program of music from our friends in other countries. Thanks to all who took part today in this broadcast presented by the Sixth Grade Class of _____ School, under the direction of Miss _____, our teacher.
Music (Cue):	Bring the music (humming of BROTHERHOOD) up in volume until cue to fade under and out.
Announcer:	(Cue) This is your School Station _____ (Letters)
Sound:	(Cue — 3 seconds later) Chimes — Do mi so do.

*   *   *   *   *

SUGGESTIONS FOR OTHER PROGRAMS

Here are some suggestions for additional themes for other types of programs. They can be chosen by the class, prepared by the committees, and presented in the classroom, the auditorium, or at the local station. They can be used as assembly programs or as programs presented for parents and the public. Music can be selected from your song book or from other sources.

1. Master Composers
2. Music of Our Own Country
3. Music of Many Lands
4. Our Neighbors to the South
5. Instruments of the Orchestra (Live performance and recordings)
6. The Different Human Voices (Live performance and recordings)
7. Music for the Dance
8. Stories in Music
9. Making Our Own Music
10. Music Brought Here by Our Families

The Meadow Butterfly

Translated from the TAGALOG by
ABBIE FARWELL BROWN and JULIA W. BINGHAM

PHILIPPINE FOLK SONG
Collected by FRANCISCA REYES-TOLENTINO

Flut-ter all the day-time, Lit-tle Pret-ty__Wing, Flut-ter all the
Pa-ru-pa-róng-bu-kid Na lí-li-pad-li-pád, Sa git-ña ng

Optional third part; imitating Double Bass

Zum zum zum zum

play-time, Lit-tle mer-ry__thing; Flut-ter from the mead-ow
da-án, Pá-pa-gá-pa-gas-pás; Sam-ba-ra ang ta-pis,

zum zum zum zum zum

Where the path-way__lies, There's a bit of shad-ow For the gay but-ter-
San-dang-kál ang mang-gás, Ang sa-yang de ko-la, Sam-piye-sa ang sa-

zum zum zum zum zum

1.
flies._____ Flut-ter all the ____
yad._____ Pa-ru-pa-róng ____

2.
See her comb made of gold,
May pay-ne-ta pa siyá

1.
zum zum zum zum

2.
zum zum

Uy! She has one, big and bold, Uy! Pet - ti-coats are swing - ing
Uy! May suk - láy pa man-dín, Uy! Nag-was de o - he - tes

zum zum zum zum

As she walks up and down. At the glass see her stand,
Ang pa - lá - la - ba-sín; Há - ha - ráp sa al - tár,

zum zum zum zum

Uy! Nod and smile, wave her hand, Then she makes a curt - sey in her
Uy! At ma - ná - na-la-mín At sa-kâ lá - la - kad Nang pa-

zum zum zum zum

beau - ti - ful gown._____ See her ____
ken - deng - ken - deng._____ May pay-

zum zum zum zum zum zum

The third part may be played as a bass, with C, F, and G₇ chords in the right hand in waltz time.

54 Come, Ye Thankful People, Come

Stanzas 1,2, HENRY ALFORD
Stanza 3, ANNA L. BARBAULD

GEORGE J. ELVEY

1. Come, ye thank-ful peo-ple, come, Raise the song of Har-vest-home;
2. All the world is God's own field, Fruit un-to His praise to yield;
3. All that spring with boun-teous hand Scat-ters o'er the smil-ing land;

All is safe-ly gath-ered in, Ere the win-ter storms be-gin;
Wheat and tares to-geth-er sown, Un-to joy or sor-row grown;
All the fruits in full sup-ply Rip-ened 'neath the sum-mer sky;

God, our Mak-er, doth pro-vide For our wants to be sup-plied;
First the blade, and then the ear, Then the full corn shall ap-pear;
All that lib-'ral au-tumn pours From her rich o'er-flow-ing stores;

Come to God's own tem-ple, come, Raise the song of Har-vest-home.
Lord of Har-vest, grant that we Whole-some grain and pure may be.
All to Thee, our God, we owe, Source whence all our bless-ings flow.

The Natural (♮) at * cancels the effect of the Sharp earlier in the measure, restoring the note, G, to its regular place in the scale.

We Thank Thee

RALPH WALDO EMERSON

GEORGE L. WRIGHT

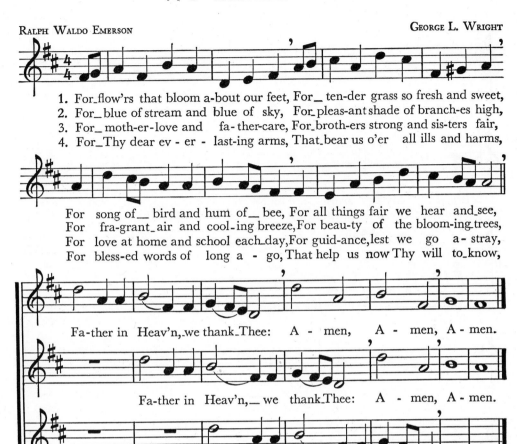

1. For flow'rs that bloom a-bout our feet, For tender grass so fresh and sweet,
2. For blue of stream and blue of sky, For pleas-ant shade of branch-es high,
3. For moth-er-love and fa-ther-care, For broth-ers strong and sis-ters fair,
4. For Thy dear ev - er - last-ing arms, That bear us o'er all ills and harms,

For song of bird and hum of bee, For all things fair we hear and see,
For fra-grant air and cool-ing breeze, For beau-ty of the bloom-ing trees,
For love at home and school each day, For guid-ance, lest we go a-stray,
For bless-ed words of long a - go, That help us now Thy will to know,

Fa-ther in Heav'n, we thank Thee: A - men, A - men, A - men.

Fa-ther in Heav'n,— we thank Thee: A - men, A - men.

Fa - ther in Heav'n,— we thank Thee: A - men.

Hymn for Home

MORAVIAN CHORALE
JOHN BALTHASAR REIMANN (1747)

NANCY BYRD TURNER

Fa - ther, may Thy bless-ing come Night and day up - on our home;
May Thy gen - tle pres-ence dwell In the place we love so well.

Bless it, roof and door and wall, Win-dow, fire-side, bless them all.
Day and night and night and day, Fa-ther, bless our home, we pray.

Lullaby

MYLES BIRKET FOSTER

The light__ is fad - ing out, Ba - by dear, Ba - by
When dark - ness cov - ers all, Love makes light, Love makes

dear; My arms__ are round thee close,____ Do not
light; God's arms__ are round us close,____ In the

fear.____ With - in our pret - ty room____ Shad - ows
night.____ The light will of - ten fade, And shad - ows

creep,__ shad - ows creep,____ Love watch - es
creep,__ shad - ows creep,____ Love al - ways

o - ver thee, Love watch - es o - ver thee,
watch - es thee, Love al - ways watch - es thee,

Sleep!____ Do__ not fear; Sleep,____ Ba - by dear!____
Sleep!____ Do__ not fear; Sleep,____ Ba - by dear!____

* The Natural (♮) is used here to caution the performer against repeating the Sharp from the previous measure.

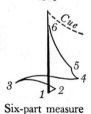

Six-part measure

The manner of conducting six-eight measure will depend upon whether the music moves slowly or quickly. When the music moves slowly, as in LULLABY by Myles Birket Foster, there are six beats to the measure and an eighth note equals one beat. When the music moves more quickly, as in CHRISTMAS AGAIN, p. 77 and HAMMOCK SONG, p. 58, there is a clear feeling of two beats to a measure, and a dotted quarter note equals one beat. This may be shown in the time signature by a figure 2 above a dotted quarter note $\frac{2}{♩.}$

Loyalty

ELEANOR GRAHAM

CHAS. MILLER

May heav'n guide my spir-it now And help me more and more, Un-
May this bright land learn ev'-ry day what loy-al sons are for, And

til no task can be too great In peace as well as war.
call on me to do my part In peace as well as war.

My Dog and I

VIRGINIA HARRISON

FOLK SONG for children,
from central ITALY

My lit-tle dog and I____ Are off____ to-geth-er
Which-ev-er way I go,____ He rush-es af-ter;

In ev-'ry kind of weath-er, Romp to-geth-er;
I al-most hear his laugh-ter, Dash-ing af-ter;

When winds are blow-ing high We fly, like rob-ins o-ver a mead-ow.
He al-most talks to me, For we are com-rades, ev-er-more rov-ing,

We love a wind-y sky,____ My lit-tle dog and I.
He's jol-ly as can be____ And such good com-pa-ny.

Telling Time

John Kendrick Bangs

Sigmund Spaeth

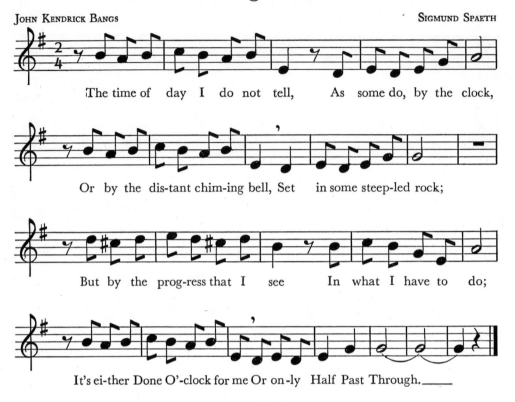

The time of day I do not tell, As some do, by the clock,

Or by the dis-tant chim-ing bell, Set in some steep-led rock;

But by the prog-ress that I see In what I have to do;

It's ei-ther Done O'-clock for me Or on-ly Half Past Through.____

Hammock Song

William Brian Hooker

Francis H. McKay

To and fro, to and fro, Under the trees my ham-mock swings,

The soft____ air hums____ with myr - i - ad wings And the

sky__ bends o - ver the earth__ be-low. To and fro, to and fro,

Swing-ing be-neath the sway-ing trees, While the qui - et voic-es of

long__ a - go__ Whis - per in__ the rus - tling breeze.

Holiday Greeting

Words and music by pupils in
Section 7-II; Raub Junior High School,
Allentown, Pennsylvania *

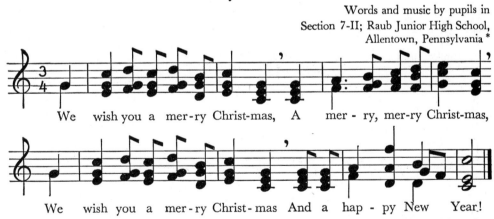

We wish you a mer-ry Christ-mas, A mer - ry, mer-ry Christ-mas,

We wish you a mer-ry Christ-mas And a hap - py New Year!

HOLIDAY GREETING, composed by school pupils in Allentown, Pennsylvania, is an
excellent example of an original melody harmonized for three parts. It is included here
because it is a good song and also because it may encourage you to compose some
music of your own. By the time you have reached the Sixth Grade you probably will
wish not only to compose short songs but also longer songs with one or more contrasting
divisions. A good way to write a longer song is to organize the divisions as follows:
I, II, I. Another good structural arrangement is: I, I, II, I. The repetition of I may be
modified where desired. Or, you may write a song in which there are verses with a
refrain. Look through the book and observe how the longer songs are organized. You
may wish to harmonize your song for two or three parts, or to write a piano accompaniment. Your studies in chording will be helpful in doing this.

* Miss Mildred Kemmerer, Supervisor

Forester's Song

SIR WALTER SCOTT   CYRIL SCOTT

The monk must a-rise when the mat-ins ring, The ab-bot may sleep to their chime, But the yeo-man must start when the bu-gles ring, 'Tis time, my heart, 'tis time._____ There's bucks and raes on Bill-hope braes, There's a herd on Short-wood Shaw,___ But a lil-y-white doe in the gar-den goes, She's fair-ly worth them a',_____ She's fair-ly worth them a'._____

The songs on pages 60 and 61 are especially appropriate for boys' voices. Cyril Scott, the distinguished contemporary English composer, has made a stirring setting of an old poem by Sir Walter Scott, "Forester's Song."

EIGHT BELLS is a lusty chantey that dates from the days of sailing ships. It has sounded over the seven seas, wherever the jolly English tar has hoisted the anchor to the rhythm of a rousing song.

Eight Bells

TRADITIONAL

ENGLISH SEA CHANTEY

Deeper voices

1. My hus-band's a sau - cy fore - top-man,   A chum of the cook's, don't you know,_____
2. My hus-band once shipped in a whal-er,   And sailed to the far north-ern seas,_____
3. And now he's no long-er a   sail - or,   He of - ten wakes up in the   night,_____

He put his head down the cook's fun-nel,   And shout-ed "Come up from be -low!"_____
But be - ing a bold-heart-ed sail- or,   He cared not for ice, sea, nor   breeze._____
And think-ing he's still on the whal- er,   Cries out with the great-est de - light:_____

REFRAIN

Eight bells!   Eight bells!   the watch from be-

Eight bells!_____ Eight bells!_____ Rouse out there the watch from be-low!_____ Eight

low! Eight bells!   Eight bells!   Rouse out there the watch from be-low!_____

bells!_____   Eight bells!_____   Rouse out there the watch from be-low!_____

Merry Christmas Bells

J. R. MURRAY

J. R. MURRAY

Chorus

1-2. Mer-ry, mer-ry, mer-ry, mer-ry Christ-mas bells, O sweet-ly, sweet-ly chime,___

Let your hap-py mu-sic on the breez-es swell, O mer-ry, mer-ry Christ-mas time.

Duet

1. Peace on earth, good will to men, O an - gel sing - ers, sing a - gain, While
2. Ban - ish ev - 'ry thought of care, Let mirth and mu - sic fill the air, Let

hearts and voic - es here be - low Send back the glad re - frain. O,
words of cheer and smiles a - bound, And glad - ness ev - 'ry - where. O,

Chorus

1-2. Mer-ry, mer-ry, mer-ry, mer-ry Christ-mas bells, O sweet-ly, sweet-ly chime,___

Let your hap-py mu-sic on the breez-es swell, O mer-ry, mer-ry Christ-mas time.

Bonnie Doon

Robert Burns

Scottish Melody

Ye banks and braes of bon-nie Doon, How can ye bloom sae fresh and fair?
Oft have I roamed by bon-nie Doon, To see the rose and wood-bine twine;

How can ye chant, ye lit-tle birds, While I'm sae wae and full of care?
To hear the birds sing of their loves, As fond-ly once I sang of mine.

Ye'll break my heart ye lit-tle birds, That wan-der through the flow'r-ing thorn;
With light-some heart I pulled a rose, A rose out of yon thorn-y tree,

Ye mind me of de-part-ed joys, De-part-ed, nev-er to re-turn.
But my false lov-er stole the rose, And left the thorn be-hind to me.

BONNIE DOON lends itself admirably to a humming accompaniment of chords, similar to
DOWN IN THE VALLEY, on page 26.

Lewis and Clark

Rosemary and S. V. Benét

Richard Donovan

1st Sopranos

Lew - is and Clark said, "Come on, let's em - bark For a
boat-ing trip up the Mis - sou - ri! _____ It's the Pres-i-dent's wish, And we
might catch a fish, Though the riv - er is mud-dy as fu - ry." _____

2nd Sopranos

So they start-ed a - way On a breez-y May day Full of
cour-age and lore sci - en - tif - ic, _____ And, be-fore they came back They had
blazed out a track From St. Lou - is straight to the Pa - cif - ic. _____

Sopranos I and 2

_____ Straight, straight, to the Pa - cif - ic. _____ And

Obbligato for voices or instruments

Glo - - ry to the

1st Sopranos

when they re-turned, It was glo-ry well-earned That they gave to the na-tion-al

2nd Sopranos

when they re-turned, They gave to__ the

rall. *a tempo*

cho - rus. Glo - - ry! And it

cho-rus._They were rag-ged and lean But they'd seen what they'd seen, And it

cho - rus glo - ry. They'd seen what they'd seen, And it

spread__ an em - pire be - fore__ us.__

spread out an em - pire be - fore__ us.__

spread out an em - pire be - fore__ us.__

PLAYING THE TUBA

The tuba is the lowest bass member of the family of brass instruments. Its deep, rich tones furnish an excellent foundation for bands, and a tuba is also used in large orchestras. You may not find one in your elementary school orchestra, but there will be one or more in the high school band.

The tuba is a long tube coiled so that it can be held in the arms as shown in the picture. John Philip Sousa, America's "March King," suggested that this tubing might be shaped in another way so that it would wind around the body of the player, the weight resting on his shoulder. The big bell was changed to face forward above the player's head. This form of the instrument is called a sousaphone, and is particularly useful for the marching band.

Tones are produced on the tuba by blowing into the instrument through a mouthpiece which is like a very large cornet mouthpiece. The part played by the tuba is quite similar to the bass part played on the piano by the left hand.

Tubas usually come in two sizes, one in the key of E-flat and another very large one in B-flat. The notes on the latter are so low that it is called the Double B-flat (BBb) tuba.

RANGE OF THE TUBA

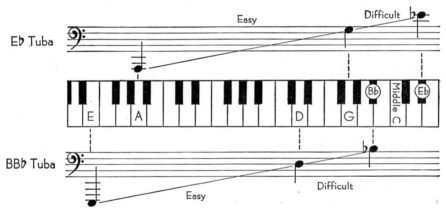

Theme: Introduction, Act III, "Lohengrin"

RICHARD WAGNER

Daisies

BLISS CARMAN

EINAR RALF

O - ver the shoul-ders and slopes of the dune_____ I

saw the white dai-sies go down to the sea, A host in the sun-shine, an

ar - my in June, The peo-ple God sends us to set our hearts free.

The bob-o-link ral-lied them up from the dell, The o-ri-oles whis-tled them

out of the wood; And all of their sing-ing was, "Earth, it is well," And

all of their danc-ing was, "Life, thou art good." O - ver the.

shoul-ders and slopes of the dune_____ I saw the white dai- sies go

down to the sea, A host in the sun - shine, an

ar - my in June, The peo-ple God sends us to set our hearts free.

The Big Bazaar

CAROLYN WELLS
"THE ANIMALS' FAIR"

MARSHALL BARTHOLOMEW

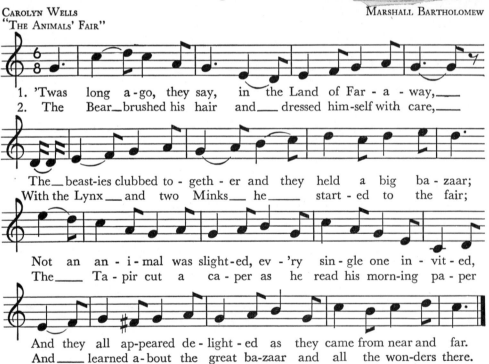

1. 'Twas long a-go, they say, in the Land of Far - a - way,____
2. The Bear__ brushed his hair and__ dressed him-self with care,____

The__ beast-ies clubbed to - geth - er and they held a big ba - zaar;
With the Lynx __ and two Minks __ he ____ start - ed to the fair;

Not an an - i - mal was slight - ed, ev - 'ry sin - gle one in - vit - ed,
The ____ Ta - pir cut a ca - per as he read his morn-ing pa - per

And they all ap-peared de - light - ed as they came from near and far.
And ____ learned a-bout the great ba-zaar and all the won-ders there.

3. The chattering Chinchilla trotted in with the Gorilla,
   Much elated, so they stated, by the prospect of the fun;
   While the Yak, dressed in black, came riding in a hack,
   And the Buffalo would scuffle, oh,— because he couldn't run.

4. The Donkey told the Monkey that he had forgot his trunk key,
   So the Ox took a box, and he put it in the way
   Of a passing Hippopotamus, who angrily said, "What a muss!"
   As he trod upon the baggage and observed the disarray.

5. Graceful little Antelope bought a delicious canteloupe,
   And at table with a Sable sat primly down to eat;
   While a frisky young Hyena coyly gave a philopena
   To an Ibex who made shy becks at her from across the street.

6. A Bison was a-pricin' a tea-chest of young hyson,
   So cheap, said the sheep, that it nearly made her weep;
   The lazy Armadillo bought a satin sofa-pillow,
   Then found a cozy, dozy place and laid him down to sleep.

7. An inhuman old Ichneumon sang a serenade by Schumann,
   The Giraffe gave a laugh and began to cheer and chaff;
   A laughing Jaguar said, "My, what a wag you are!"
   And the Camel got his camera and took a photograph.

8. The Baboon and the Loon and the rollicking Raccoon
   Fed the Otter with a blotter, though it wasn't good to eat;
   The Bunny thought 'twas funny all his money went for honey,
   But a Rabbit has a habit of liking what is sweet.

9. The Ape left her cape out on the fire-escape,
   The Jereboa lost her boa, which caused her much distress;
   But the fair was well attended and the money well expended,
   And financially and socially it was a great suceess.

70

Oh Come, All Ye Faithful
(*Adeste Fideles*)

LATIN HYMN, 17TH CENTURY
Translated by REV. FREDERICK OAKELEY

JOHN READING

1. Oh come, all ye faith - ful, Joy - ful and tri - um - phant!
2. Sing, choirs of an - gels, Sing in ex - ul - ta - tion,
3. Yea, Lord, we greet Thee, Born this hap - py morn - ing;
Ad - es - te, fi - de - les, Lae - ti tri - um - phan - tes;

Oh come ye, oh come ye to Beth - le - hem;
Sing, all ye cit - i - zens of Heav'n a - bove;
Je - sus, to Thee be glo - ry giv'n;
Ve - ni - te, ve - ni - te in Beth - le - hem;

Come and be - hold Him Born the King of an - gels;
Glo - ry to God In the high - est;
Word of the Fa - ther, Now in flesh ap - pear - ing;
Na - tum vi - de - te Re - gem an - ge - lo - rum.

Oh come, let us a - dore Him, Oh come, let us a - dore Him,
Ve - ni - te, a - do - re - mus, Ve - ni - te, a - do - re - mus,

Oh come, let us a - dore Him, Christ the Lord.
Ve - ni - te, a - do - re - mus, Do - mi - num.

*The Natural (♮) is explained on page 85.

The First Nowell

TRADITIONAL

TRADITIONAL

1. The first Now-ell the an-gel did say
2. They look-ed up and saw a star
3. And by the light of that same star
4. This star drew nigh to the north-west,
5. Then en-tered in those Wise Men three

Was to cer-tain poor shep-herds in fields as they lay;
Shin-ing in the East be-yond them a-far,
Three Wise Men came from a coun-try a-far,
O'er Beth-le-hem it took its rest,
Full rev-'rent-ly up-on their knee,

In fields where they lay keep-ing their sheep
And to the earth it gave a great light,
To seek for a king was their in-tent,
And there it did both stop and stay,
And of-fered there in His pres-ence

On a cold win-ter's night that was so deep.
And so it con-tin-ued both day and night.
And to fol-low the star wher-ev-er it went.
Right o-ver the place where Je-sus lay.
Their gold and myrrh and frank-in-cense.

DESCANT

Now-ell, Now-ell, Now-ell, Now-ell,

Born is the King of Is-ra-el.

The Wassail Song

TRADITIONAL

ENGLISH FOLK SONG

Two swings to a measure

1. Here we come a - was - sail-ing A - mong the leaves so
2. We are not dai - ly beg - gars That beg from door to
3. Good Mas - ter and Mis - tress As you sit by the
4. God bless the mas - ter of this house, Like-wise the mis - tress,

green,— Here we come a wan-d'ring, So fair— to be seen.
door,— But we are neigh-bors' chil-dren Whom you have seen be-fore.
fire,— Pray think of us poor chil-dren Who wan-der in the mire.
too;— And all the lit - tle chil-dren That round the ta - ble go.

72

Love and joy come to you, And to you your was- sail, too, And God bless—you, and send— you a hap - py new year, And God send— you a hap - py new— year.

73

Le Marin
(*The Mariner*)

Translated from the FRENCH of
JACQUELINE KRIEGER by
ELEANOR ALLETTA CHAFFEE

ARTHUR HONEGGER

Mon père est un ma - rin vo-guant sou-vent vers un pa-ys loin-
My fa - ther sails the sea, Go-ing on voy-ag-es hap-py and

tain. Bien qu'a pei-ne je le con-nais-se très grande est ma ten-dres-se pour
free. But I see my fa-ther so sel-dom Yet, ah, he is so wel-come to

lui. Cha-que fois, au re - tour, il m'offre a - vec a-
me. Ev -'ry time he is here He is ev - er more

mour un ca-deau ma-gni-fi - que.   Ne croi-rais - je
dear, For he brings me a pres - ent.   *Strange he seems, though*

pas chi-mé - ri - que Sans   ce sou - ve - nir sé - dui-sant
al - ways so pleas - ant; Yes,   *I can be - lieve it is he*

ce pa - pa d'un in - stant.
Com - ing home from the sea.

The piano accompaniment to the song LE MARIN lends itself admirably to an interesting
treatment. The melody may be sung by a solo voice or a semi-chorus of light voices.
The chords in the right hand may be hummed in three parts by most of the class, while
a few deeper voices sustain Middle C as a continuous undertone. A sustained tone
below changing chords is called an "organ point." Such vocal treatment of this selection will make a good concert number, especially by a choir of selected voices.

Round the Campfire

Mary Budlong

Folk Song from Russia

Come, my com-rades, gath-er round the camp-fire, Sing a song to - geth - er;
Come, my com-rades, gath-er round the camp-fire, Cheer the night with sing - ing.

Sing a song a-round the blaz-ing camp-fire, What care we for storm-y weath - er!
In the fire - light, by the roll-ing riv-er, Home-ward now our hearts are wing-ing.

Sing a song a-round the blaz-ing camp-fire, What care we for storm-y weath - er!
In the fire - light, by the roll-ing riv-er, Home-ward now our hearts are wing-ing.

Christmas Again

NANCY BYRD TURNER

FOLK SONG from CZECHOSLOVAKIA

1. Car - ol, car - ol, Christ-mas is here, Set the mu - sic
2. Watch a star that trav-els to-night, Send - ing beau - ty
3. Car - ol, car - ol, Christ-mas is come, Tell the old, old

ring - ing, Lift the song so sil - ver - y clear,
down - ward, Like the star whose won - der - ful light
sto - ry; Clear and near and o - ver each home

An - gels once were sing - ing, An - gels once were sing - ing.
Led the Wise Men on - ward, Led the Wise Men on - ward.
Shines the an - cient glo - ry, Shines the an - cient glo - ry.

Vocal Chording

God Rest You Merry, Gentlemen

TRADITIONAL

OLD ENGLISH CHRISTMAS CAROL

1. God rest you mer - ry, gen - tle - men, Let
2. In Beth - le - hem, in Jew - ry, This
3. From God our heav'n - ly Fa - ther A

noth-ing you dis - may, Re - mem-ber Christ our Sav - iour Was
bless - ed Babe was born, And laid with - in a man - ger Up-
bless - ed an - gel came, And un - to cer - tain shep - herds Brought

born on Christ-mas Day, To save us all from Sa - tan's pow'r When
on this bless -ed morn; The which His moth-er Ma - ry Did
tid - ings of the same; How that in Beth - le - hem was born The

CHORUS

we were gone a - stray.
noth-ing take in scorn. Oh,____ tid - ings of com - fort and
Son of God by name.

joy, com-fort and joy, Oh,____ tid - ings of com - fort and joy.

4. "Fear not then," said the angel,
   "Let nothing you affright,
   This day is born a Saviour
   Of a pure virgin bright,
   To free all those who trust in Him,
   From Satan's pow'r and might."

5. The shepherds at those tidings
   Rejoiced much in mind,
   And left their flocks a-feeding,
   In tempest, storm, and wind,
   And went to Bethlehem straightway,
   The Son of God to find.

6. And when they came to Bethlehem,
   Where our dear Saviour lay,
   They found Him in a manger
   Where oxen feed on hay,
   His Mother Mary kneeling down
   Unto the Lord did pray.

7. Now to the Lord sing praises,
   All you within this place,
   And with true love and brotherhood
   Each other now embrace;
   This holy tide of Christmas
   All other doth deface.

Joy to the World

ISAAC WATTS

GEORGE FREDERICK HANDEL

1. Joy to the world! the Lord is come, Let earth re-
2. Joy to the earth! the Sav-iour reigns, Let men their
3. No more let sins and sor-rows grow, Nor thorns in-
4. He rules the world with truth and grace, And makes the

ceive her King; Let ev-'ry___ heart___ pre-pare___ Him___
songs em-ploy, While fields___ and___ floods,___ rocks, hills,___ and___
fest the ground; He comes_ to___ make___ His bless-ings___
na-tions prove The glo-ries___ of___ His right-eous-

room,___ And heav'n and na-ture__ sing, And_heav'n and na-ture_
plains___ Re-peat the sound-ing_ joy, Re-peat the sound-ing_
flow___ Far as the curse is___ found, Far__ as the curse is___
ness,___ And won-ders of His__ love, And_won-ders of His__

And heav'n and na-ture sing, And
Re-peat the sound-ing joy, Re-
Far as the curse is found, Far
And won-ders of His love, And

sing, And__ heav'n,__ and heav'n___ and na-ture sing.
joy, Re-peat,__ re-peat___ the sound-ing joy.
found, Far__ as,___ far as___ the curse is found.
love, And__ won-ders, won-ders of His love.

heav'n and na-ture sing And heav'n and na-ture sing.
peat the sound-ing joy, Re-peat the sound-ing joy.
as the curse is found, Far as the curse is found.
won-ders of His love, And won-ders of -His love.

Morning Song

C. H. RINK

1. Soft - ly, gen - tly break - ing, Comes the morn's first ray,
2. Then a peace - ful still - ness Fills the soul a - gain,

And with smiles the sun - shine___ Ush - ers in the day.
Heal - ing all its sor - row,___ Sooth-ing all its pain.

3. Life is earnest, truly,
   And the pilgrim's road;
   But with heart confiding
   I look up to God.

4. He who me created
   Gave me life and breath,
   Lovingly shall guide me
   Through the gates of death.

Hymn of the Orange Free State

H. A. L. HAMELBERG
HERMANN JACOBSON, TR.

W. F. G. NICOLAI

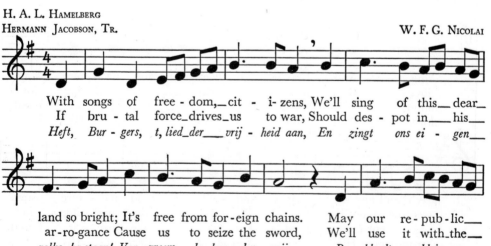

With songs of free - dom,_cit - i- zens, We'll sing of this_ dear_
If bru - tal force_drives_us to war, Should des - pot in___ his_
*Heft, Bur - gers, t, lied_der___ vrij - heid aan, En zingt ons ei - gen_*

land so bright; It's free from for - eign chains. May our re - pub - lic___
ar - ro-gance Cause us to seize the sword, We'll use it with_the_
volks - be-staan! Van vreem - de ban - den vrij, Be - kleedt ons klein_ ge. -

ev - er live, It's built on or - der,— law and right, And
li - on's strength, Pro - tect our home_with— vig - i - lance, For
mee - ne - best, Op or - de, met— en— regt ge - vest, Rang

Free - dom on - ly reigns, And Free - dom on - ly reigns.
Lib - er - ty's our Lord, For Lib - er - ty's our Lord.
in der Sta - ten rei, Rang in der Sta - ten rei.

Serenade

NANCY BYRD TURNER   FOLK SONG from southern FRANCE

Gai - ly my light gui - tar is sound - ing Un - der your
Low is the moon, the world in slum - ber, Soft - ly I

win - dow dim— and high, Strik-ing the strings I lift a
touch my light— gui - tar; Un - der the stars that have no

bal - lad, Bal-lad of dream - y days— gone by. Deep in the
num - ber You will look down, the fair - est star. Now in the

wood a bird has wak-ened, Whip-poor-will, loud and clear,—
wood the bird is si - lent, Learn-ing my mel - o - dy,—

Clear-er and near - er yet my mu - sic You— will hear.
Come to your win - dow, then, and soft - ly An - swer me!

The distinguished French organist and composer, Théodore Dubois, has written a well-known
organ work based on this theme — "Fantasietta with Variations."

Song of the Mermaid

From the opera, "OBERON"
by CARL MARIA VON WEBER (1786-1826)

Andante con moto

O,_____ 'tis pleas - ant to float___ on the crest,___ Of the
O,_____ 'tis pleas - ant to float___ on the crest,___ Of the

wea - ried waves_ as they sink_____ to rest.___ Slow - ly the
wea - ried waves_ as they sink_____ to rest.___ Pac - ing his

rays___ of the sun___ have fled,___ Stars___ are shin - ing
rounds_ at the twi - light hour,_ Moves___ the guard_ through

o - ver-head.___ The night_ breeze comes_ with its
time - worn tow'r.___ And signs___ him - self___ as he

breath___ so bland, All lad - en with sweets_from the dis - tant
breathes__ a pray'r, Then lis - tens a - while_ to the witch - ing

land.___ O,_____ 'tis pleas - ant to float_____ a - long,___
air.___ O,___ 'tis pleas - ant to float_____ a - long,___

Comb - ing our locks___ as we sing_____ our song.___
Comb - ing our locks___ as we sing_____ our song.___

A STRANGE COINCIDENCE

At the time young Mendelssohn was writing the delightful overture to Shakespeare's "Midsummer Night's Dream" in 1826, an older composer, Weber, in another part of Germany, had just completed the music for his famous opera, "Oberon." These two composers, both writing music about Oberon, used an identical musical theme.

From the Overture, "MIDSUMMER NIGHT'S DREAM"
by FELIX MENDELSSOHN-BARTHOLDY

Violins I and II

Joys of Winter

MARTHA DABNEY

FRANZ MAIR

Tra la, tra la, tra la!_____ The sleigh bells make__ a mer-ry chime!
Tra la, tra la, tra la!_____ The skat-ers mer - ry mu-sic make,

Tra la, tra la, tra la!_____ They ring the praise__ of win-ter time!
Tra la, tra la, tra la!_____ Out skat-ing on____the fro-zen lake!

Down hill - sides white__ the col - ored sleds Go dash-ing, flash-ing,
They glide, they curve,__ they fol - low fleet As if the wind__ were

blues and reds; A nip is in the frost - y air And hearts____ are
in their feet; Their mu - sic ech - oes like a rhyme As on_____ they

light_____ With laugh - ter ev - 'ry - where.
go,_____ Oh, hap - py win - ter time!

Autumn Song of the Birds

From the original by
MARY BUDLONG

MARTTI TURUNEN
FINNISH COMPOSER

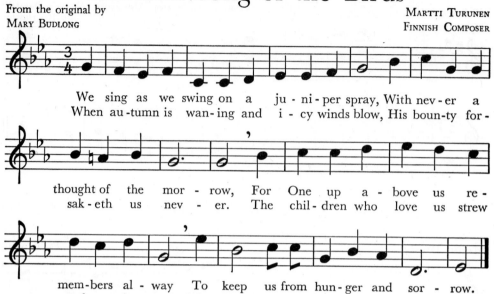

We sing as we swing on a ju-ni-per spray, With nev-er a
When au-tumn is wan-ing and i-cy winds blow, His boun-ty for-

thought of the mor-row, For One up a-bove us re-
sak-eth us nev-er. The chil-dren who love us strew

mem-bers al-way To keep us from hun-ger and sor-row.
crumbs on the snow; May bless-ings a-bide with them ev-er.

Evening Song

ELLEN WALES WALPOLE

FOLK SONG from STUTTGART (1879)

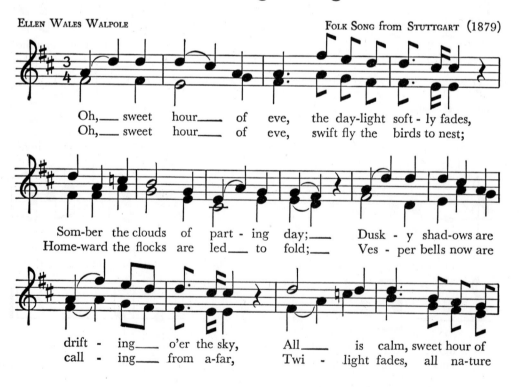

Oh,___ sweet hour___ of eve, the day-light soft-ly fades,
Oh,___ sweet hour___ of eve, swift fly the birds to nest;

Som-ber the clouds of part-ing day;___ Dusk-y shad-ows are
Home-ward the flocks are led___ to fold;___ Ves-per bells now are

drift-ing___ o'er the sky, All___ is calm, sweet hour of
call-ing___ from a-far, Twi-light fades, all na-ture

twi - light shades,___ All is calm, sweet hour of twi - light shades.
finds its rest,___ Twi - light fades, all na-ture finds its rest

Sunday Song

Nancy Byrd Turner   H. Gackslatter

1. On Sun-day when I wak - en   It's dif-f'rent ev-'ry - where;___
2. The mu-sic's deep and sol - emn,   Yet glad and sweet to__ hear;___
3. All days are meant for glad - ness,   All days are meant to__ bless;___

A soft, new light is   in the world, A mu-sic__ in the   air.
The light that lies up - on   the hills   Is beau-ti - ful - ly   clear.
But Sun-day dawns up - on   the earth With spe -cial_love -li - ness.

5 #5 — 6 5   4 #4 5 4

One of the music signs you will meet frequently is the Natural (♮). A curious thing about
the natural is that under different circumstances it has three meanings:
1. When the natural appears on a line or space which has been flatted by the key
signature, it tells us to sing or play one half-step higher. In this case the natural is
similar to a sharp. See Autumn Song of the Birds.
2. When the natural appears on a line or space which has been sharped by the key
signature, it tells us to sing or play one half-step lower. In this case the natural is
similar to a flat. See Evening Song.
3. Where an accidental sharp or flat has been used, the sign (♮) restores the line or
space to its natural pitch. See Sunday Song. The scale numbers below the staff
will help you to read the chromatic passage.
Like other chromatic signs, the natural affects only the measure in which it appears, although sometimes you will find it at other places as a cautionary sign.

The New Day

Nancy Byrd Turner

Folk Song from Finland

1. The morn-ing o - pens__ ear - ly, The shad - ows slip a - way,
2. From wood and mead-ow,__ bright-ly, The birds be - gin to sing;
3. There's light on hill and__ hol-low, The winds are up and fleet,

The earth lies white and__ pearl - y, A mir-ror__ for__ the day.
The dew is shak-en__ light-ly From ev -'ry__ leaf - y thing.
The roads that we shall__ fol-low Are wait-ing__ for__ our feet.

Refrain

A new day now is break-ing, O Lord of all the days,

Thy hap-py chil-dren,__wak-ing, Send up a__ song__of__ praise.

In the earlier books of New Music Horizons much emphasis has been given to various kinds of creative activities. One suggested creative project has been to have you write new additional verses for songs. In doing this, careful study was necessary in order to fit the words to the notes, to bring word emphases on the stronger parts of the measure, and to make the rhyming scheme agree with the phrase relationship in the song. Of course the spirit of your new text should express the spirit of the music. This type of creative expression may be continued with certain songs in the Sixth Book. But here it may be expanded to include writing a completely new poem to go with a given song. The noble and dignified music of THE NEW DAY may well suggest another religious setting; or it may suggest a school or class hymn. Nearly every class has talented pupils who enjoy expressing the fine spirit of loyalty and fellowship which their classmates feel to their school and to each other.

Dancing

Virginia Harrison   Folk Song from Mexico

Time for danc-ing! Tune the fid-dle! Call the
Time for danc-ing! Fid-dle's hum-ming, Laugh-ter's

dan-cers, clear a space! Right and left, now, in the
ring-ing ev-'ry-where. Down the cen-ter two are

mid-dle, Ev-'ry cou-ple takes its place.
com-ing, Feet are trip-ping light as air.

Chorus

Dance a-way, O, dance a-way to and fro; Dance a-
Dance with me, O, dance with me and be whirled Like a

way and in and out, heel and toe, To a bright tune,
leaf, a-long the way gai-ly twirled; And in time, too,

to a light tune, To a quick tune off we go!
like a rhyme, too; It's the fin-est in the world!

Captain Jinks

W. H. LINGARD

T. MACLAGAN

1. I'm ___ Cap - tain Jinks of the Horse Ma-rines; I feed my horse on
2. I ___ joined my corps ___ when twen-ty-one, Of course I thought it
3. The ___ first day I ___ went out to drill The bu-gle sound made
4. My ___ tai-lor's bills ___ came in so fast, Forced me one day to

corn ___ and beans, ___ And sport ___ young la - dies in their teens, Though a
cap-i-tal fun; When the en-e-my came, of course I run, For I'm
me ___ quite ill; 'At the bal - ance step, my hat it fell, And that
leave ___ at last; ___ And la - dies, too, no more did cast ___? Sheep's

cap - tain in ___ the Ar - my. I teach young la-dies how to dance, ___
not cut out for the Ar - my. When I left home, Ma-ma, she cried, Ma-
would-n't do for the Ar - my. The of - fi-cers they all did shout, ___
eyes at me in the Ar - my. My cred - i-tors at me did shout, At

How to dance, ___ how to dance, I teach young la-dies how to dance, For
ma, she cried, Ma-ma, she cried, When I left home, Ma-ma, she cried, "He's
All cried out, ___ all cried out, The of - fi-cers they all did shout, "Oh,
me did shout, at me did shout, My cred - i-tors at me did shout, "Why,

CHORUS

I'm the pet of the Ar - my. I'm ___ Cap - tain Jinks of the
not cut out for the Ar - my!" I'm ___ Cap - tain Jinks of the
that's the cure for the Ar - my!" I'm ___ Cap - tain Jinks of the
kick him out of the Ar - my!" I'm ___ Cap - tain Jinks of the

Horse Ma-rines; I feed my horse on corn and beans, And

of - ten live be-yond my means, Though a cap-tain in the Ar - my.

CAPTAIN JINKS is often danced while singing the following words:

Captain Jinks came home last night,
Pass your partner by the right,
Swing your neighbor so polite,
For that's the style in the army.
All join hands and circle left,
Circle left, circle left,
All join hands and circle left,
For that's the style in the army.

(For Chorus, repeat the first four lines.)

Formation: Circle; all holding hands. Boys have their partners on their right.

Figure: All take one stamping step forward, followed by another step (measure 1). Take two steps back to place; drop hands (measure 2). Partners pass each other by the right shoulders, each boy thus proceeding to the partner of the boy on his right, and each girl meeting the boy on the left of her first position (measures 3 and 4). Swing new partners (measures 5, 6, and 7). Face in, single circle, boys having new partners on their right (measure 8). All join hands and walk or skip around in clockwise direction (measures 9-16, inclusive). For chorus, repeat as directed for first eight measures.

Repeat as long as desired.

A Patriotic Creed

EDGAR A. GUEST

KAY KELLOGG

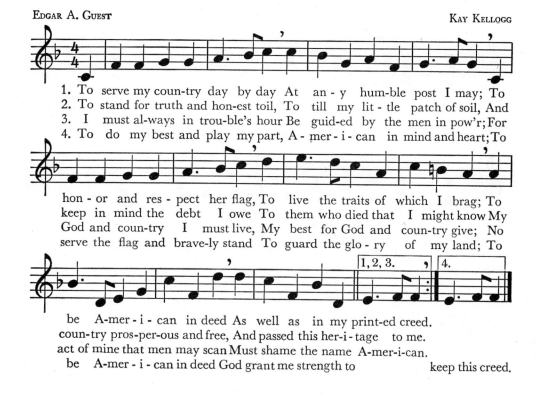

1. To serve my coun-try day by day At an-y hum-ble post I may; To
2. To stand for truth and hon-est toil, To till my lit-tle patch of soil, And
3. I must al-ways in trou-ble's hour Be guid-ed by the men in pow'r; For
4. To do my best and play my part, A-mer-i-can in mind and heart; To

hon-or and res-pect her flag, To live the traits of which I brag; To
keep in mind the debt I owe To them who died that I might know My
God and coun-try I must live, My best for God and coun-try give; No
serve the flag and brave-ly stand To guard the glo-ry of my land; To

be A-mer-i-can in deed As well as in my print-ed creed.
coun-try pros-per-ous and free, And passed this her-i-tage to me.
act of mine that men may scan Must shame the name A-mer-i-can.
be A-mer-i-can in deed God grant me strength to keep this creed.

Patriotic Song

TRADITIONAL SCOTTISH TUNE,
"SCOTS WHA' HAE"

OLD TRADITIONAL VERSES

Friends, we bid you wel - come here, Free - dom's sa - cred
Who is he, de - void of shame, Jus - tice for him -

cause re-vere; Dai - ly breathe a prayer sin-cere For
self would claim, Yet de - ny to all the same Through

them who suf - fer wrong. Fear not, lest your hope should fail,
vain and self - ish pride? Friends, you long our hearts have known;

Truth is strong and must pre-vail. What though foes our
You're not left to fight a-lone; We will make the

cause as - sail, They'll nev - er pros - per long.
cause our own, For heav'n is on our side.

The rhythm of the dotted eighth and sixteenth notes has been studied in earlier grades. Be careful to hold the dotted eighth note its full value, and to sing the sixteenth note very quickly just before the following note.

Mistress Sally

Ellen Wales Walpole

Folk Song from Norway

1. Sal - ly, Mis - tress Sal - ly, Way up in Hak - ke Val - ley,
2. Sal - ly, Mis - tress Sal - ly, Way up in Hak - ke Val - ley,
3. Sal - ly, Mis - tress Sal - ly, Way up in Hak - ke Val - ley,

Time to call the cows and Fetch the milk-ing stool. Fill the pails and car - ry
Half a pound of cheese curds From a quart of milk. Squeeze it tight and pat it,
Half a pound of but - ter From a quart of cream. Then the churn she wash - es

Sal - ly, Sal - ly, Sal - ly,

To the dair - y cool. Sal - ly, bus - y Sal - ly!
Strain it through the silk. Sal - ly, clev - er Sal - ly!
In a lit - tle stream. Sal - ly, tir - ed Sal - ly.

Sal - ly,

Vocal Chording

The Golden Vanity

TRADITIONAL

ENGLISH FOLK BALLAD

1. There was a ship came from the north coun-try, And the
2. Then up there came a lit - tle cab-in boy, And he
3. "Oh, I will give you sil-ver and I will give you gold, And my
4. Then the boy made him read-y, and o-ver-board sprang he, And he

name of the ship was *The Gold - en Van - i - ty,* And they
said to the skip-per,— "What will you give to me, If I
on - ly daugh-ter your bride to be, If you'll
swam a - long - side of the Turk - ish en - e - my; And

feared she might be tak - en by the Turk - ish en - e - my, That
swim a - long - side of the Turk - ish en - e - my, And
swim a - long - side of the Turk - ish en - e - my, And
with his au - ger sharp in her side he bored holes three, And he

sails up-on the Low-land, Low-land, that sails up-on the Low-land sea.
sink her in the Low-land, Low-land, and sink her in the Low-land sea?"
sink her in the Low-land, Low-land, and sink her in the Low-land sea."
sank her in the Low-land, Low-land, and sank her in the Low-land sea.

CHORUS

Verses 1-6

Low - land, Low - land, She's sail-ing in the Low - land

Verse 7

sea. She's sail - ing in the Low - land sea.

5. Then the boy turned around, and back again swam he,
   And he cried out to the skipper of *The Golden Vanity;*
   But the skipper did not heed, for his promise he would need;
   And he left him in the Lowland sea.

6. Then the boy swam round, and came to the port side,
   And he looked up at his messmates, and bitterly he cried:
   "O, messmates, take me up, for I'm drifting with the tide
   And I'm sinking in the Lowland sea."

7. Then his messmates took him up, but on the deck he died.
   And they sewed him in his hammock that was so large and wide;
   And they lowered him overboard, but he drifted with the tide,
   And sank beneath the Lowland sea.

This famous old English ballad was brought to many parts of our country by the early settlers. It is still sung in a number of different versions; the one given here came from the southern Appalachian Mountains.

Winter Quarters
(Mormon Hymn)

WILLIAM CLAYTON

Melody adapted from
an ENGLISH song

1. Come, come, ye saints, no toil nor la-bor fear, But with joy, Wend your way;
2. Why should we mourn, or think our lot is hard? 'Tis not so, All is right!
3. We'll find the place which God for us pre-pared, Far a-way, In the West,

Though hard to you this jour-ney may ap-pear, Grace shall be As your day!
Why should we think to earn a great re-ward, If we now Shun the fight?
Where none shall come to hurt nor make a-fraid; There the saints Will be blessed.

'Tis____ bet-ter far____ for us to strive,___ Our use-less cares___ from
Gird___ up your loins,___ fresh cour-age take,___ Our God will nev - er
We'll__ make the air____ with mu-sic ring,___ Shout prais-es to____ our

us to drive. Do this and joy your hearts will swell: All is well! All is well!
us for-sake; And soon we'll have this tale to tell: All is well! All is well!
God and King; A-bove the rest these words we'll tell: All is well! All is well!

Themes from "España Waltz"
by E. Waldteufel

In 1883 Alexis Emmanuel Chabrier and his wife went on a tour through Spain. The lovely folk music that they heard so charmed the composer that he jotted many of the melodies down in his notebook. On returning to their home in Paris, Chabrier worked out his musical impressions of Spain into a composition for two pianos which he later arranged for orchestra. The brilliant "España" created a sensation and at once established Chabrier as one of the leading composers of France. His Rhapsody became so celebrated that, about 1890, the famous Parisian composer, Emile Waldteufel, arranged the melodies as a waltz, much as the popular composers of today rewrite some of the greatest melodies of the masters into song hits. Waldteufel was one of the few waltz composers who rivaled the prestige of the Viennese Waltz King, Johann Strauss. Waldteufel's "España Waltz" is still enjoyed wherever beautiful waltzes are played. You will be interested to hear both Waldteufel's popular waltzes and the original versions of these Spanish melodies in Chabrier's "España," and to compare the way they are treated by two skillful composers.

Morning
(*Caro mio ben*)

Paraphrased from the ITALIAN by
ELLEN WALES WALPOLE

GIUSEPPE GIORDANI

Come, dear-est one, Day has be - gun. Lis - ten, be-
Oh, how I long For your sweet song, Long for the
Ca - ro mio ben cre - di - mi al - men sen - za di

lov - ed, to___ my song.___ Wake, dear - est
morn - ing with___ its joy.___ For your sweet
te___ lan - gui-sce il cor.___ Ca - ro mio

one, Lis-ten, be-lov-ed,_to___ my song. Hark to my
song, Long for the morn-ing_with_ its joy. Voic - es of
ben sen - za di te___lan - gui - sce il cor. Il tuo fe-

voice, Wake and re - joice,___ Hear my sweet song_ nor_ turn___ a-
spring, Ech - o and ring,___ Join-ing your song_ to_ wake___ my
del so - spi-ra o-gnor___ ces - sa cru - del___ tan - to___ ri-

96

way. Hear my sweet song, turn not a - way,___ turn not a-
heart. Join - ing your song, wak - ing my heart,___ wak - ing my
gor. Ces - sa cru - del tan - to ri - gor___ tan - to ri-

way. Come, dear - est one, Day has be - gun, Lis - ten, be-
heart. Oh, how I long For your sweet song, Long for the
gor. Ca - ro mio ben cre - di - mi al - men sen - za di

lov - ed,_ to___ my song. Come, dear - est one, Day has be-
morn - ing_with___ its joy. Oh, how I long For your sweet
te_ lan - gui - sce il cor. Ca - ro mio ben cre - di - mi al-

gun, Lis - ten, be - lov - ed, to___ my song.
song, Long for the morn - ing with___ its joy.
_men; sen - za di te___ lan - gui - sce il cor.

Songs Great Artists Sing. Both the English and the Italian words are given for this celebrated song. The Italian language is particularly well suited for singing because of the
predominance of core vowel sounds. You will enjoy learning to sing in both languages.
Try to make your voices rich and expressive with the Italian words. Then carry the same
tone quality over into the English words.

Hail, Evening Bright

Queen Marie Antoinette of France
Transcribed by J.B.T. Wekerlin

1. Hushed in si - lence, eve - ning___ clos - es

2. High the sil - ver moon___ is___ soar - ing
3. Hills and val - leys, cool - ing___ breez - es,

On the bus - y scenes___ of___ toil, And bright

In the blue ex - panse___ of___ sky, Swift her
Flush with life ere dawns___ the___ morn; Slum - b'ring

na - ture ___ soon com - pos - es In - to___

pale ef - ful - gence pour - ing On earth's
beau - ty nev - er ceas - es Charms her

rest__ her__ teem - ing soil. Still - ness a - round,

fair - est scen - er - y. Pil - lowed to rest,
fea - tures to a - dorn. Hail! eve-ning bright,

si - lence pro-found! Eve - ning has earth in slum - ber

na - ture op-pressed, Eve - ning re - stores with fa - vors
soft glows thy light, Eve - ning, oh, leave us thy de-

bound, Eve - ning has earth__ in __ slum - ber bound.

blest, Eve - ning re - stores__ with__ fa - vors blest.
light, Eve - ning, oh, leave__ us__ thy de - light.

Shusti-Fidli

ENGLISH version by
LILIAN JACKSON and FJERIL HESS

CZECH musical
instrument game song

Chil-dren, guess what I have here. Tell us, tell us, fa-ther dear.

A fid-dle to make mu-sic gay. Fa-ther, tell us how you play.

Shus - ti fid - li fid - li, Shus - ti fid - li fid - li, Here's how the

fid - dle plays, Shus - ti fid - li fid - li, Shus - ti fid - li fid - li,

*Skip 2 measures for Final ending *Final ending.

1st time, father
2nd time, children

Here's how it plays. Here's how it plays. Diu-dli diu-dli-em,

Diu - dli diu - dli-em, Here's how { the / it clari - net plays, plays.____

Tra-da-da, Tra-da-da, Here's how { the / it trum-pet plays, plays.____

Brmm-fitz-fitz, Brmm-fitz-fitz, Here's how { the / it bass viol plays, plays.____

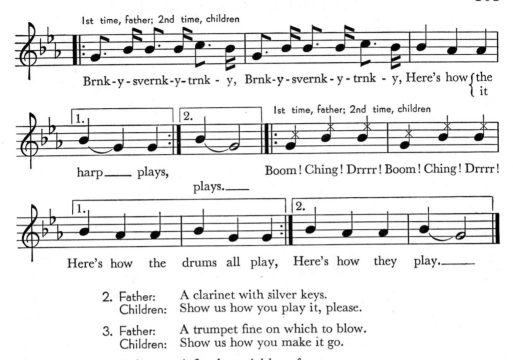

1st time, father; 2nd time, children

Brnk-y-svernk-y-trnk-y, Brnk-y-svernk-y-trnk-y, Here's how {the / it

harp___ plays, plays.___

1st time, father; 2nd time, children

Boom! Ching! Drrrr! Boom! Ching! Drrrr!

Here's how the drums all play, Here's how they play.___

2. Father: A clarinet with silver keys.
   Children: Show us how you play it, please.

3. Father: A trumpet fine on which to blow.
   Children: Show us how you make it go.

4. Father: A fine bass viol here for you.
   Children: Show us how to play it too.

5. Father: A golden harp with colored strings.
   Children: Show us, father, how it rings.

6. Father: A big bass drum and cymbals round.
   Children: Show us how to make them sound.

After each instrument, all the preceding instruments are repeated in reverse order; for instance, after chorus 4 add choruses 3, 2 and 1. The two endings of the drum chorus are sung to the lower notes on the last line of the music; the higher notes are for the second ending of the fiddle chorus with which the song ends.

Who'll Buy My Posies?

Four-Part Round

From the FRANKLIN SQUARE COLLECTION

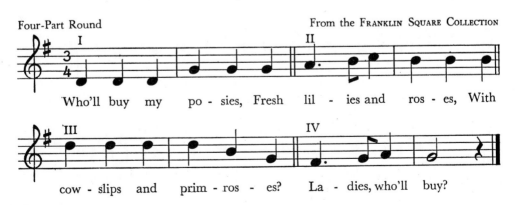

Who'll buy my po - sies, Fresh lil - ies and ros - es, With

cow - slips and prim - ros - es? La - dies, who'll buy?

Afternoon on a Hill

EDNA ST. VINCENT MILLAY

JOHAN HYE-KNUDSEN

I will be the glad - dest thing Un - der the sun! I will
And when lights be - gin to show Up from the town, I will

touch a hun - dred flow - ers And not pick one.
mark which must be mine_____ And then start down.

I will look at cliffs and clouds With qui - et eyes, Watch the

wind bow down the grass And the grass_____ rise.

Dawn and Sunset

C. H. CRANDALL

SILCHER

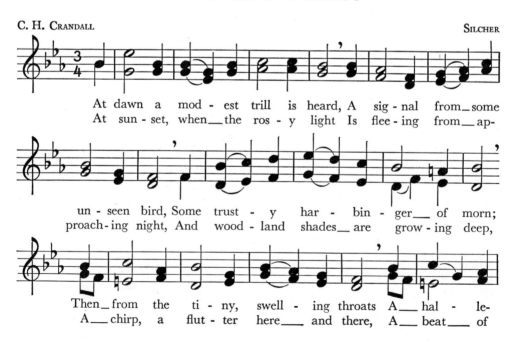

At dawn a mod - est trill is heard, A sig - nal from__ some
At sun - set, when__ the ros - y light Is flee - ing from__ ap-

un - seen bird, Some trust - y har - bin - ger__ of morn;
proach - ing night, And wood - land shades__ are grow - ing deep,

Then__ from the ti - ny, swell - ing throats A__ hal - le-
A__ chirp, a flut - ter here____ and there, A__ beat__ of

lu - jah of rich - est notes In greet - ing to the
wings___ up - on___ the air, And night has hushed the

day just born, In greet - ing to___ the day just born.
birds to sleep, And night___ has hushed__ the birds to sleep.

The Return of the Birds

Abba D. Willard   Ethelbert Nevin

Child

1. Lit - tle bird, on wea - ry pin - ion, Sign and pledge of
2. Cour - age, sweet, the sun is shin - ing; Teach no les - son
3. Pret - ty birds, we'll sing to - geth - er, Bright or cloud - y

Spring's do - min - ion, Her - ald of thy tune - ful throng,
of re - pin - ing; Hark! a rush - ing in the air,
be the weath - er, Gai - ly, 'mid the blos - soms sweet,

Bird

Why so plain - tive is thy song? Bleak and chill the north winds blow,___
Song and glad - ness ev - 'ry - where. Chil - dren, join our cho - rus sweet,___
Brave - ly in the storm and sleet, Ne'er for - get - ting through the whole,___

1-2

Bud and leaf - let fear the snow; Though your call we hailed with glad-ness,
Spring is near, on danc-ing feet,___ From the sun - ny South-land greet-ing
Heart of bird, or hu - man soul;___ Praise to Him, whose love un-sleep-ing,

1-2-3

All my song is turned___ to sad - ness.
Buds are op - 'ning, lambs___ are bleat - ing.
Holds His crea - tures in___ His keep - ing.

Chinese National Anthem

Dr. Sun Yat-Sen
Translated by Tu Ting Hsiu
Edited by committee

Ch-eng Mao Yün

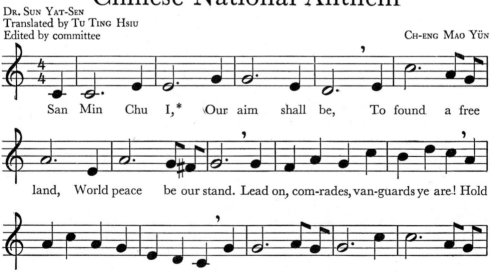

San Min Chu I,* Our aim shall be, To found a free land, World peace be our stand. Lead on, com-rades, van-guards ye are! Hold fast your aim by sun and star! Be ear - nest and brave, Your coun - try to

save.　One heart,　one＿ soul;　One mind,　one＿ goal!

* Pronounced San Min Joo Ee, Three Principles of the people.

Meng Chiang Nü's Lament

S. H. CHEN

Arranged by C. H. Y. CHEN

Plum flow'rs＿＿ ev - 'ry-where,　spring＿is draw-ing near,＿＿
Win - ter＿＿＿ ush - ers in　ice＿＿ and＿＿ snow,＿＿
Ts'eng chi＿＿＿ mei＿＿ hua,　tsieh＿ sing＿＿＿＿ ts'eng,

Lan-terns　are＿ lit＿＿ at ·　ev - 'ry＿front＿ door,＿＿
Meng Chiang Nü＿ toils＿ a　thou - sand＿miles＿ through;＿
Chia chia＿＿＿ hu＿ hu　ti hung＿＿＿＿ teng,

Each＿ man　with＿his＿ wife＿　lives＿in＿peace at home,＿＿
A - lone I＿＿＿＿＿ trudge,＿　for＿I＿ hear the call＿＿
Zeng＿ chia zang＿＿＿ fu＿　tö＿ yö＿＿＿＿ zi,＿＿

Mine＿a - lone has＿ gone＿ to＿＿ build the＿ Great＿ Wall.＿＿
Of＿ my love＿＿ dy - ing＿ by the＿ Great＿ Wall.＿＿
Mang＿ Chiang Ngu ke＿ zang＿ fu＿＿ zao zang＿＿＿＿ zeng.＿＿

Welcome to the New Year

ELEANOR FARJEON

VIRGIL THOMSON

Hey, my lad, ho, my lad! Here's a new broom. Heav-en's your

house-top And Earth is your room. Tuck up your shirt sleeves, There's

plen-ty to do; Look at the mud-dle That's wait-ing for you!

Dust in the corn-ers And dirt on the floor, Cob-webs still

cling-ing To win-dow and door. Hey, my lad, ho, my lad!

Nim-ble and keen, Here's your New Broom, my lad, See you sweep clean.

The Song of the Happy Farmer

ELIZABETH BENNETT

ROBERT SCHUMANN

With joy I sing The mir - a - cle of Spring: A prom - ise true of life a - new The warm days bring. In sum - mer days I give my grate - ful praise For sun and rain And grow - ing grain And cows a - graze. When

day is done, I count my rest well won. Then

in the fall I reap my har-vests all, And

firm and fast A-wait at last The win-ter's call. The

days are chill, But I am hap-py still; Though

wind   and snow   In   win - ter   bliz-zard blow,   My

heart   so   gay Will keep   for   aye The   sum - mer   glow..

The piano part of THE SONG OF THE HAPPY FARMER is given just as it was written for the piano by Robert Schumann. The voice part and the words have been added to Schumann's composition. Most young piano students are acquainted with this piece. It is included here not only because it makes an excellent song, but also to encourage young pianists to play accompaniments for the singing of their friends and classmates.

For A' That and A' That

ROBERT BURNS   ANCIENT SCOTTISH SONG

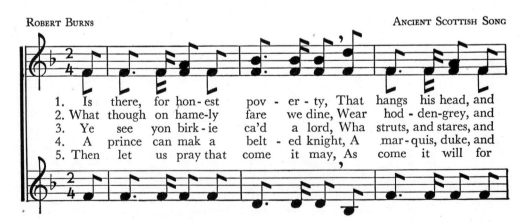

1. Is   there, for hon - est   pov - er - ty, That   hangs   his head, and
2. What though on hame-ly   fare   we dine, Wear   hod - den-grey, and
3. Ye   see   yon birk - ie   ca'd   a lord, Wha   struts, and stares, and
4. A   prince can mak a   belt - ed knight, A   mar - quis, duke, and
5. Then   let   us pray that   come   it may, As   come   it will for

a'_____ that? The cow - ard slave, we pass him by, We
a'_____ that; Gie fools their silks, and knaves their wine, A
a'_____ that; Tho' hun - dreds wor - ship at his word, He's
a'_____ that; But an hon - est man's a - boon his might, Guid
a'_____ that; That sense and worth, o'er a' the earth May

dare be poor for a'_____ that! For a'_____ that, and
man's a man for a'_____ that. For a'_____ that, and
but a coof for a'_____ that. For a'_____ that, and
faith he mau - na fa'_____ that! For a'_____ that, and
bear the gree, and a'_____ that. For a'_____ that, and

a'_____ that, Our toils ob - scure, and a'___ that; The
a'_____ that, Their tin - sel show, and a'___ that; The
a'_____ that, His rib - bon, star, and a'___ that, The
a'_____ that, Their dig - ni - ties, and a'___ that, The
a'_____ that, It's com - ing yet, for a'___ that, That

rank is but the guin - ea stamp; The man's the gowd for a'___ that.
hon - est man, tho' e'er sae poor, Is king o' men for a'___ that.
man of in - de - pend - ent mind, He looks and laughs at a'___ that.
pith o' sense, and pride o' worth, Are high - er rank than a'___ that.
man to man, the world___ o'er, Shall broth - ers be for a'___ that.

Little Things

ELIZABETH BENNETT

FOLK SONG from YUGOSLAVIA

Key of C Minor, Normal Form

1. Lit - tle vio - let, pret - ty flow - er, None can see thee grow - ing,
2. Ti - ny pearl of beau - ty rar - est, How can I com - pare_____ thee?
3. Ripe red ber - ries, wood - land treas - ure, Thy de - lights are wast - ed,

But with oth - ers, in a___ bow - er, What a love - ly show - ing!
In a neck - lace thou are_ fair - est When a queen doth wear__thee.
But a king would know real_ pleas - ure If thy sweets he tast - ed.

The Key of C Minor
Normal (Natural) Scale

1	2	3	4	5	6	7	8
C	D	E♭	F	G	A♭	B♭	C

In the earlier books of this series you have sung many songs in minor keys. You probably will remember SONG OF THE VOLGA BOATMEN, MINKA, and WHEN JOHNNY COMES MARCHING HOME. What do these songs express? How would you describe the minor melody on this page? The Normal Minor Scale sounds as though you sang with the syllables from **la** to **la** of the major scale, which is the way it is taught by many teachers. If you sing this scale with a neutral syllable, or hum it, you will observe that the particular effect called minor is due chiefly to 3 and 6 of the scale, each of which is a half-step lower than in the major scale. In the Normal Minor Scale, 7 is also flatted, that is, there is a step between 7 and 8, instead of a half-step as in the major scale. Some people sing the Normal Minor Scale using the syllables from **do** to **do**. When sung this way, or with the pitch names or numbers, you must be careful to give the correct minor sounds of 3, 6, and 7. You will notice in the Normal Minor Scale that the half-steps occur between 2 and 3, and between 5 and 6. This will give you a plan for building Normal Minor Scales from any keynote, and for deriving the proper key signatures. You should learn to think of minor keys as being individual, and not dependent on major keys. However, they do have certain relationships. The major and minor keys having the same key signature are called Relative. The key of C minor is relative to the key of E-flat major. The major and minor keys having the same keynote (although the key signatures are different) are called Tonic (Parallel). What is the tonic major key of C minor?

Desert Song

ELEANOR ALLETTA CHAFFEE

DERVISH SONG from EGYPT

Key of E Minor, Normal Form

On the des-ert sands I find
I have nev-er seen her face,

Where I dance, the pat-tern lined
But my ea-ger eyes can trace

Of the one who went_be - fore me,
Where my shad-ow weaves_and_cir-cles,

Oh, my love, the gyp-sy wind!
All her tan - ta-liz-ing grace.

The Seasons Come, the Seasons Go

NANCY BYRD TURNER

JEAN SIBELIUS
FINNISH COMPOSER

Key of D Minor, Normal Form

The sea-sons come, the sea-sons go, And__ God has
The weath-er is the plan of God; He__ sends the

planned them all.
frost and snow,

He makes the win-ter wind to blow, The__
The pleas-ant rain up-on the sod Where_

au-tumn leaves to fall;
wheat and bar-ley grow.

And when the balm-y spring-
And then the long year fol -

time De-scends on wood and hill,
lows Like an-swer to His call,

His word goes forth, the
And ev-'ry time is

leaves re-turn, And grass and bud and daf-fo-dil.__
bless-ing time, For God has wise-ly planned them all!__

Three Apples

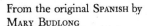

From the original SPANISH by
MARY BUDLONG

FOLK SONG from SPAIN

The Key of C Minor, Harmonic Form

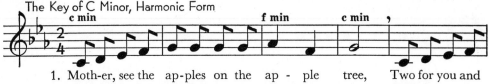

1. Moth-er, see the ap-ples on the ap - ple tree, Two for you and
2. Now the wind is stir-ring in the ap - ple tree, Brisk-ly it is
3. Soon we'll have a feast be-neath the ap - ple tree, Ripe and red and

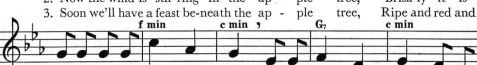

Fa-ther, and there's one for me! Oh, there's one for me, count-ing
blow-ing from the dis - tant sea, Oh, for you and me, it is
juic-y are the ap - ples three, Oh, the ap - ples three are for

one, two, three, So red and so high on the ap - ple tree.
blow - ing free, And ap - ples hang ripe on the ap - 'ple tree.
you and me, We'll all have a feast 'neath the ap - 'ple tree.

THE KEY OF C MINOR

Harmonic Scale

1	2	3	4	5	6	7	8
C	D	Eb	F	G	Ab	B♮	C

Sometimes a more effective ending to a minor melody is obtained by changing 7 so that it sounds only one half-step below 8. Also in chording this gives a more satisfying V_7 chord. You will notice that half-steps occur between 2 and 3, between 5 and 6, and between 7 and 8, indicated by ⌣. From 6 to 7 there is a wide interval of a step-and-a-half, indicated by +. This will give you a plan for building Harmonic Minor Scales in other keys and for playing accompaniments with the three principal chords in minor keys.

Chording in the Key of C Minor

Chording in the Key of A Minor

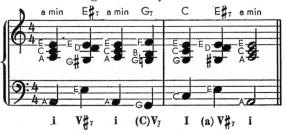

To Mother
(*Du gamle mor*)

Paraphrased from the original
NORWEGIAN by ELEANOR ALLETTA CHAFFEE.

EDVARD GRIEG

Key of A Minor, Harmonic Form

My moth-er's heart is warm and gay, And she will nev - er
I can-not tell her how I feel, Yet some-times in her
Du gam - le mor, du sli - ter arm, so svei - ten er som

know____ How dear she is from day to day, Wher -
eyes____ An un - der-stand - ing seems to steal That
blod,____ men en - då i ditt hjar - ta varm, og

ev - er I__ may go, may go, Wher - ev - er I may go.____
is__ both sweet and wise, and wise, That is both sweet and wise.____
du__ meg gav__ min ster - ke arm og det - te vil - le mod.____

Ballad of the Homebound Ship

Paraphrased from the original BULGARIAN
by MARTHA DABNEY

BULGARIAN NATIONAL SONG

Key of A Minor, Harmonic Form

1. Deep - ly flows the si - lent Dan - ube, With its sol - emn
2. Though the storms have marred her beau - ty, Beat - ing mast__ and
3. "Cour-age" was the flag she car - ried, High through wind__ and

tide, Bring - ing back a____ ship that's wan - dered
sail, See the light on__ ea - ger fac - es
foam; Joy's the ban - ner__ at her mast - head,

Long and far and wide,____ wide.
Crowd - ing at the rail,____ rail.
Proud - ly bear - ing home.____ home.

THE HARP

The harp is one of the most beautiful of musical instruments, with its graceful curves and many strings of different lengths. It is used both as a solo instrument and in the orchestra. It is effective both in a large ensemble and in a small group of instruments.

The performer on the harp plucks the strings with his fingers. By playing on different parts of the string and by other devices, the tone quality may be varied. Also there are pedals which raise or lower the pitch of the strings. The compass of the harp is virtually the same as the compass of the piano.

Not many high school orchestras include a harp, for it is very difficult to play. But over the radio and in recorded selections the harp is heard quite frequently, and you will enjoy recognizing its tone in the instrumental ensemble.

There are numerous beautiful and effective passages for the harp in great orchestral works. One of the most familiar of these examples is the harp cadenza at the beginning of the "Waltz of the Flowers," from Tschaikowsky's well-known "Nutcracker" Suite. Another charming harp cadenza is found in the overture to "Mignon," by Ambroise Thomas.

George Nelidoff Photo   *Courtesy Lyon and Healy*

Waltz of the Flowers

PETER I. TSCHAIKOWSKY

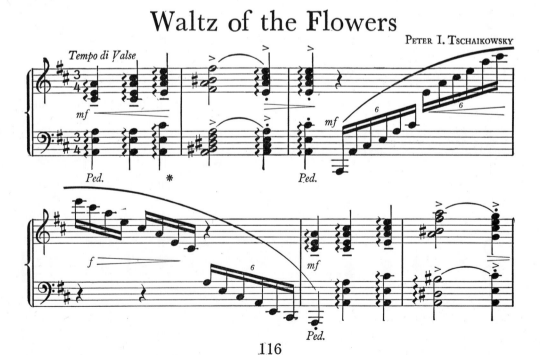

At this place in the music nearly every harp player varies this cadenza to suit his own taste. But he always closes the passage as follows:

Angels Ever Bright and Fair

From the oratorio "Theodora" by
George Frederick Handel

An-gels ev-er bright and fair,   An-gels ev-er bright and

fair,   Take, O   take   me,   Take, O   take me   to your

care,_____   Take me,   take, O   take me,   An - gels___

ev - er bright and__ fair,   Take,   O   take me__ to__ your care,

Take,   O   take me   to   your____   care.

Songs Great Artists Sing. This is one of Handel's most famous airs. It is sung wherever beautiful music is cultivated. Observe that it should be sung slowly, that there are eight beats to the measure, and that an eighth note equals one beat. In the original composition the melody as given above is followed by a contrasting section, and then by a return to this first section, thereby presenting the structural pattern which we know as three-part form.

A composer is free to choose the kind of note he wishes to represent the value of a beat. The lower figure of the time signature shows his choice. Most of the songs you have studied use the quarter note to represent the value of a beat: $\frac{2}{4}$ $\frac{3}{4}$ $\frac{4}{4}$. But you will also find music in which the beat is represented by an eighth note: $\frac{3}{8}$ $\frac{6}{8}$ $\frac{4}{8}$. Where this is the case, the other notes represent sounds of proportionate length.

ANGELS EVER BRIGHT AND FAIR, although having a time signature of $\frac{4}{4}$, is always sung an eighth note to a beat, that is, it is always sung as though the time signature were $\frac{8}{8}$, eight beats to a measure, each beat represented by the value of an eighth note. You will find other songs in this book in which an eighth note represents the value of a beat.

Sailor's Song

NANCY BYRD TURNER

FOLK SONG from SWEDEN

Deep the o - cean, wild and wide, Wa - ter round us
Wea - ry flows the end - less tide, E'en the wind is
Man - y a storm be - sets our sail, Foam and fu - ry
Per - il smites with ev - 'ry gale, But we meet it

on - ly;
lone - ly.
fling - ing,
sing - ing.

Night is black and land is far,
Hearts are light when hearts are brave;

But we steer by one good star, Straight press - ing
We will laugh at wind and wave. Let tem - pest

on! Un - til our port is won.
come! They bear us near - er home!

Oh Me, Poor Chap!

Translated from the original
Estonian by Olly Kukepuu

Old Estonian Folk Melody
arranged by J. Aavik

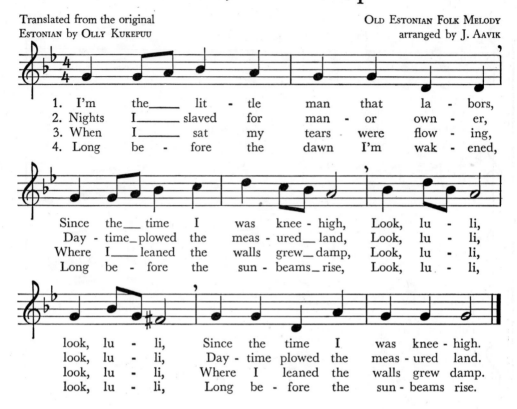

1. I'm the___ lit - tle man that la - bors,
2. Nights I___ slaved for man - or own - er,
3. When I___ sat my tears were flow - ing,
4. Long be - fore the dawn I'm wak - ened,

Since the___ time I was knee - high, Look, lu - li,
Day - time_plowed the meas - ured___ land, Look, lu - li,
Where I___ leaned the walls grew___ damp, Look, lu - li,
Long be - fore the sun - beams_ rise, Look, lu - li,

look, lu - li, Since the time I was knee - high.
look, lu - li, Day - time plowed the meas - ured land.
look, lu - li, Where I leaned the walls grew damp.
look, lu - li, Long be - fore the sun - beams rise.

My Beautiful Forest

Paraphrased from the Bulgarian
by Elizabeth Bennett

Folk Song from Bulgaria

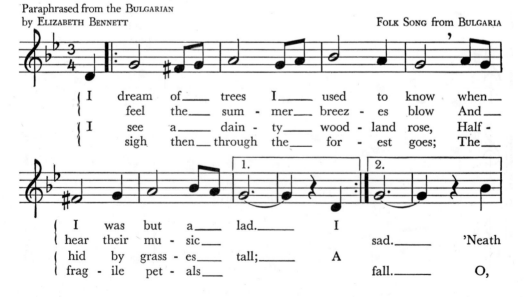

I dream of___ trees I___ used to know when___
feel the___ sum - mer___ breez - es blow And___
I see a___ dain - ty___ wood - land rose, Half -
sigh then___ through the___ for - est goes; The___

1.
2.

I was but a___ lad.___ I
hear their mu - sic___ sad.___ 'Neath
hid by grass - es___ tall;___ A
frag - ile pet - als___ fall.___ O,

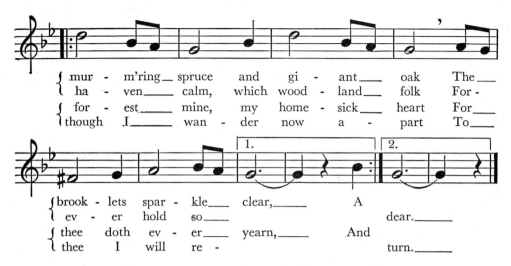

{ mur - m'ring spruce and gi - ant oak The
{ ha - ven calm, which wood - land folk For -
{ for - est mine, my home - sick heart For
{ though I wan - der now a - part To

1.   **2.**

{ brook - lets spar - kle clear, A
{ ev - er hold so dear.
{ thee doth ev - er yearn, And
{ thee I will re - turn.

Snow on the Mountain

MARTHA DABNEY   FOLK SONG from SWEDEN

The snow on the moun-tain-top is there till late in spring,
The snow on the moun-tain-top is white a-gainst the sky,

What a love-ly thing! There's green on the mead-ow Where
Pure and cold and high. We see gold and crim-son Where

win-ter long has gone; The snow on the moun-tain stays on.
flow-ers flame be-low, And high on the moun-tain the snow.

Chording in the Key of F Minor

i   ii°   V♮   i   (A♭) V₇   I   V   (f) V♮₇   i

122 Let Us With a Gladsome Mind

Chorale

JOHN MILTON

Harmonized by
FRANZ SILCHER

1. Let___ us,___ with a glad - some mind, Praise__ the
2. He,___ with___ all - com - mand - ing might, Filled__ the
3. All___ things__ liv - 'ing He doth feed; His___ full
4. Let___ us,___ then, with glad - some mind, Praise__ the

Lord,__ for He is kind;
new - made world with light. For His___ mer - cies shall en-
hand__ sup - plies their need.
Lord,__ for He is kind;

dure, Ev - er faith - ful, ev - er sure.

Sometimes a composer chooses a half note to represent the value of a beat: $\frac{2}{2}$ $\frac{3}{2}$ $\frac{4}{2}$. Where this is the case, the other notes represent sounds of proportionate length.

Oh Worship the King

R. GRANT

Attributed to
GEORGE FREDERICK HANDEL

1. Oh wor-ship the King, all glo-rious a - bove! Oh grate-ful - ly
2. Oh tell of His might! Oh sing of His grace! Whose robe is the
3. Thy boun-ti - ful care, what tongue can re - cite? It breathes in the
4. O meas-ure-less Might! in - ef - fa - ble Love! While an-gels de-

sing His pow'r and__His love! Our shield and de - fend- er, the
light, Whose can - o - py, space. His char-iots of wrath the deep
air, it shines in__the light; It streams from the hills, it de-
light to hymn Thee__ a - bove, The hum-bler cre - a-tion, though

An-cient of Days, Pa - vil-ioned in splen-dor, and gird-ed with praise.
thun-der-clouds form, And dark is His path on the wings of the storm.
scends to the plain, And sweet-ly dis - tils in the dew and the rain.
fee - ble their lays, With true ad - o - ra-tion shall lisp to Thy praise.

The sturdy third voice-part of this splendid hymn is excellent for the voices of those boys who have well rounded lower tones. Indeed, it is quite appropriate at this time to begin thinking of the time ahead when boys' voices begin changing into men's voices. One of the ways to prepare for future tenor and bass voices is to sing the third part in such three-part songs as this one. You will observe that not all the tones are deep. What is wanted is not coarse growling, but mellow tones that maintain an even quality throughout the voice compass while occasionally dipping into the lower range of the voice.

The Pretty Plowboy

TRADITIONAL

ENGLISH FOLK SONG

1. As___ I was a - walk - ing one morn-ing fair in spring,____
2. There's the lark in the morn - ing, she ris - es from her nest,_____
3. When the day's work is o - ver that he has got to do,_____

I___ heard a pret - ty dam - sel so sweet - ly to sing,
And she mounts the white___ air with___ dew___ ,on her breast,
Per - haps to some___ wake or_____ coun-try fair he'll go,

And___ as she was a - sing-ing, these___ words I heard her say,_____
And___ like the pret-ty plow-boy she'll whis-tle and she'll sing,_____
And___ with___ his___ sweet-heart he'll___ dance___ and he'll sing,_____

"There's no life ____ like the plow-boy's in the sweet___ month of May."
And at night she will re - turn_____ to her nest___ back a - gain.
For a plow-boy is as hap - py as a prince___ or a king.

Weevily Wheat

Dance Directions

Formation: Four couples in longways formation, all facing the top. Step: Quiet skip throughout.

1. Each couple takes crossed hands. Head couple turns short to left and goes to bottom, followed by other couples (8 counts). Again short to left and up the center to original places (8 counts).

Refrain: Head couple cast away from each other and, followed by others, go to bottom, meeting partner (8 counts). Cast away again, return outside to original places (8 counts).

2. Boys' line goes to right half way around girls' line (8 counts). Each boy turns left about and all return to places. Refrain. 3. Girls' line the same, around the boys' line. Refrain.

4. Boys' line all the way around the girls' line. Refrain. 5. Girls' line all the way around the boys' line. Refrain.

6. Boys join hands in a ring and go clockwise; on counts 7 and 8 balance and then return counterclockwise to places in line. Refrain. 7. Girls do the same, but go counterclockwise first and then clockwise. Refrain.

8. All join hands in one big ring, go clockwise; balance on counts 7 and 8 and then return counterclockwise to places. Refrain.

When all five stanzas of the song have been sung, go back to the beginning and sing as many more stanzas as are necessary to end the dance.

Weevily Wheat

AMERICAN FOLK SONG
Tune from an old ENGLISH COUNTRY DANCE

TRADITIONAL

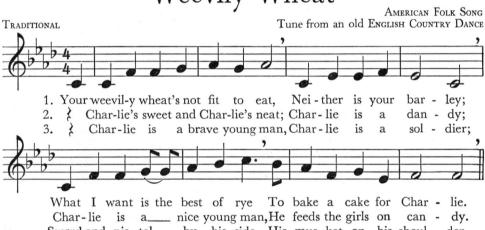

1. Your weevil-y wheat's not fit to eat, Nei-ther is your bar - ley;
2. Char-lie's sweet and Char-lie's neat; Char - lie is a dan - dy;
3. Char-lie is a brave young man, Char - lie is a sol - dier;

What I want is the best of rye To bake a cake for Char - lie.
Char - lie is a___ nice young man, He feeds the girls on can - dy.
Sword and pis - tol___ by his side, His mus-ket on his shoul - der.

REFRAIN

Rise you up in the morn-ing, All to-geth - er ear - ly;

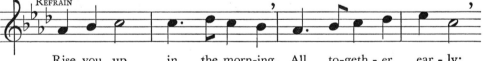

You need not be at all a-fraid, In-deed I love you dear - ly.

4. Over the river to feed my sheep,
   Over the river to Charlie,
   Over the river to feed my sheep,
   And measure up my barley.

5. The higher up the cherry tree,
   The riper grows the cherry;
   The sooner boys and girls will court,
   The sooner they will marry.

125

Old Joe Clark

Traditional

American Folk Song

1. ⅞ Old Joe Clark was a mean old man, I'll   tell you the rea-son why,
2. ⅞   I don't like_____ old Joe Clark, I   nev-er__ think I   shall;
3. I   went up on the__ moun-tain top To   give my_ horn a   blow;

He   ran a-cross my gar-den plot   And tore down all my   rye.
⅞   I don't like_____ old Joe Clark, But I   al-ways liked his   gal.
⅞ Thought I heard my sweet-heart say,_____ "Yon-der comes my beau!"

Chorus

Fare ye well,_____ old Joe Clark,   Fare ye well, I   say;

Fare ye well,_____ old Joe Clark, I'm goin' a-way to   stay.

Fiddle Tune (may be whistled)

4. The 'possum in the 'simmon tree,
   The raccoon on the ground,
   The raccoon said, "You rascal, you,
   Shake them 'simmons down."

5. The jay-bird in the sugar tree,
   The sparrow on the ground,
   The jay-bird shake the sugar down,
   The sparrow passed it round.

6. The jay-bird and the sparrow hawk,
   They flew all round together;
   Had a fight in the briar patch,
   And never lost a feather.

7. The jay-bird died with the whooping cough,
   The sparrow with the colic;
   Along came a turtle with a fiddle on his back,
   Inquiring the way to the frolic.

* The down-stem indicates a quarter note. In stanzas with only one syllable at this point, the quarter note is sung and the following notes are omitted.

Twenty, Eighteen

Traditional

English Folk Song

1. "Ho! yon - der stands a charm - ing crea - ture,
2. "Ho! Mad - am, I am come for to court you,
3. "Ho! Mad - am, I have rings and jew - els,
4. "Ho! What care I for your rings and jew - els?

Who she is I do not know; I'll go and court her
If your fa - vor I may gain; And if you will
Mad - am, I have house and land, Mad - am, I have
What care I for your house and land? What care I for your

for her beau - ty, Un - til she do say yes or no."
en - ter - tain me Per - haps I may come this way a - gain."
wealth of treas - ures; All shall be at your com - mand."
wealth of treas - ures? All I want is a hand - some man."

Instruments or Voices

Ah!

Instruments or Voices

Ah!

Twen-ty, eigh-teen, six - teen, four-teen, Twelve, ten, eight, six, four, two, naught;

Nine-teen, seven-teen, fif - teen, thir-teen, E-lev-en, nine and sev-en, Five, three, and one.

In the Land of the Incas

INCA FOLK SONG
from ECUADOR

ELIZABETH BENNETT

Very slowly Key of D minor, Normal Form

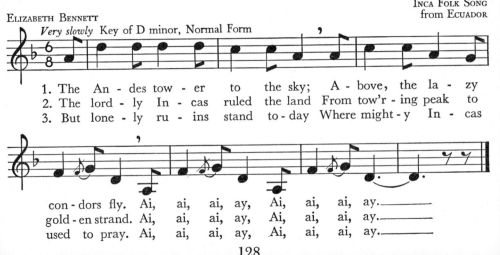

1. The An - des tow - er to the sky; A - bove, the la - zy
2. The lord - ly In - cas ruled the land From tow'r - ing peak to
3. But lone - ly ru - ins stand to - day Where might - y In - cas

con - dors fly. Ai, ai, ai, ay, Ai, ai, ai, ay.____
gold - en strand. Ai, ai, ai, ay, Ai, ai, ai, ay.____
used to pray. Ai, ai, ai, ay, Ai, ai, ai, ay.____

128

Garden Song

Arthur Guiterman

Marion Bauer

Bee balm for humming-birds, Ros-es for the bee, Lark-spur for but-ter-flies And

Ros-es for the bee, Lark-spur for but-ter-flies And

Bee balm for humming-birds, Ros-es for the bee, Lark-spur for but-ter-flies And

hol-ly-hocks for me; Blue flax for or-i-oles To mend their hang-ing nests, But

hol-ly-hocks for me; Blue flax for or-i-oles To mend their hang-ing nests,

hol-ly-hocks for me,__for me; Blue flax To mend their hang-ing nests,

bee balm for humming-birds, Our ev-er wel-come guests,__Our wel-come guests.

Bee balm for humming-birds, Our ev-er wel-come guests,__Our wel-come guests.

Bee balm for humming-birds, Our ev-er wel-come guests,__Our wel-come guests.

Cockles and Mussels

TRADITIONAL

OLD IRISH AIR

Six beats in a measure.

1. In Dub - lin's fair ci - ty, where girls are so pret - ty, I
2. She was a fish-mon - ger, but sure, 'twas no won - der, For
3. She died of a "fa - ver," and no one could save her; And

first set my eyes on sweet Mol - ly Ma-lone, As she
so were her fa - ther and moth - er be - fore; And they
that was the end of sweet Mol - ly Ma-lone; Her____

wheeled her wheel-bar - row through streets broad and nar - row Cry-ing,
each wheeled their bar - row through streets broad and nar - row Cry-ing,
ghost wheels her bar - row through streets broad and nar - row Cry-ing,

"Cock - les and mus - sels! A - live, a - live oh!

CHORUS

A - live, a-live oh!____ A - live, a - live oh!"____ Cry-ing,

"Cock - les and mus - sels, a - live, a - live oh!"

Father, We Bring Thee Our Praises

NANCY BYRD TURNER

OLD GERMAN CHORALE

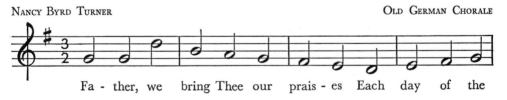

Fa - ther, we bring Thee our prais - es Each day of the

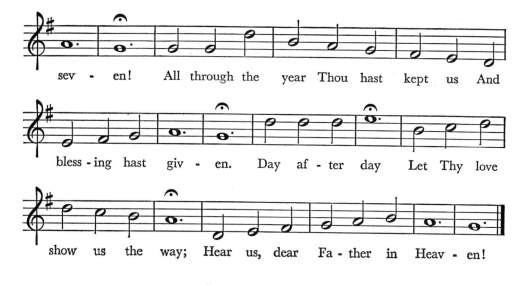

sev - en! All through the year Thou hast kept us And

bless - ing hast giv - en. Day af - ter day Let Thy love

show us the way; Hear us, dear Fa - ther in Heav - en!

A Winter Song

ELIZABETH BENNETT

OLD GERMAN FOLK MELODY

1. { Oh, why should you be griev - ing Up - on this win - ter___ day?
{ The chill winds are de - ceiv - ing, At heart the world is___ gay.

2. { The song-birds have de - part - ed; The flow - ers all are___ dead.
{ But be not so down-heart - ed, Seek win - ter joys in - stead.

{ See how the sun-shine stream - ing Fills all the woods_with_ light;
{ The snow - y fields are gleam - ing With jew - els spar - kling_ bright.

{ The spar-rows chirp in cho - rus Up - on the leaf - less___ tree.
{ With such brave cheer be-fore ___ us , We too should cheer-ful___ be.

Willow Whistles

Virginia Harrison

Folk Song from Russia

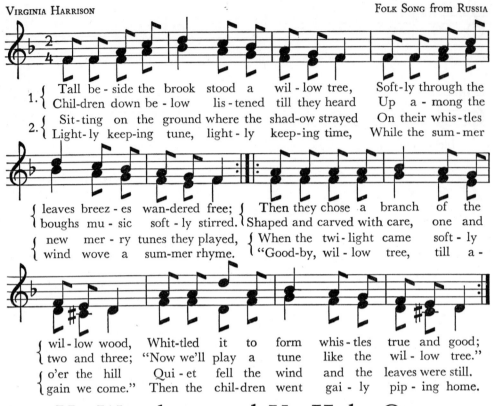

1. { Tall be-side the brook stood a wil-low tree, Soft-ly through the
   { Chil-dren down be-low lis-tened till they heard Up a-mong the

2. { Sit-ting on the ground where the shad-ow strayed On their whis-tles
   { Light-ly keep-ing tune, light-ly keep-ing time, While the sum-mer

{ leaves breez-es wan-dered free; } Then they chose a branch of the
{ boughs mu-sic soft-ly stirred. } Shaped and carved with care, one and
{ new mer-ry tunes they played, { When the twi-light came soft-ly
{ wind wove a sum-mer rhyme. } "Good-by, wil-low tree, till a-

{ wil-low wood, Whit-tled it to form whis-tles true and good;
{ two and three; "Now we'll play a tune like the wil-low tree."
{ o'er the hill Qui-et fell the wind and the leaves were still.
{ gain we come." Then the chil-dren went gai-ly pip-ing home.

Ye Watchers and Ye Holy Ones

Paraphrased from the Latin
by Athelstan Riley

Old Hymn (XVI Century)

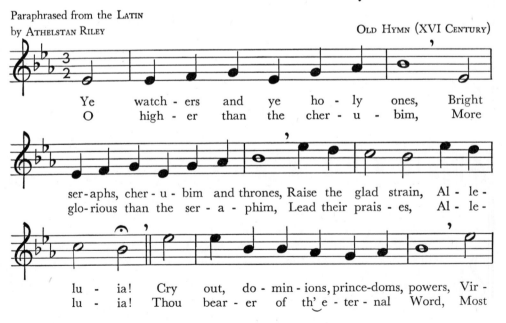

Ye watch-ers and ye ho-ly ones, Bright
O high-er than the cher-u-bim, More

ser-aphs, cher-u-bim and thrones, Raise the glad strain, Al-le-
glo-rious than the ser-a-phim, Lead their prais-es, Al-le-

lu-ia! Cry out, do-min-ions, prince-doms, powers, Vir-
lu-ia! Thou bear-er of th' e-ter-nal Word, Most

tues, arch - an - gels, an - gels' choirs, Al - le - lu - ia, Al - le -
gra-cious, mag - ni - fy the Lord, Al - le - lu - ia, Al - le -

lu - ia, Al - le - lu - ia, Al - le - lu - ia, Al - le - lu - ia!

Seventeen Come Sunday

ENGLISH FOLK BALLAD

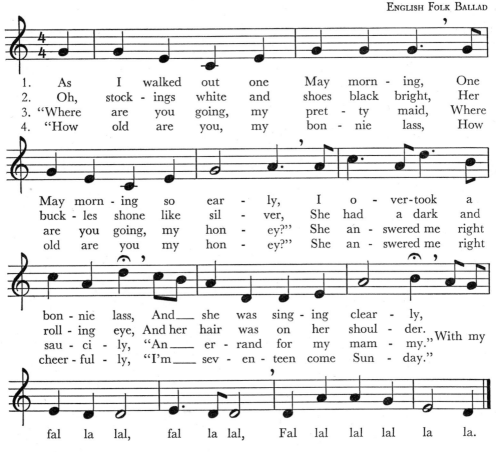

1. As I walked out one May morn - ing, One
2. Oh, stock - ings white and shoes black bright, Her
3. "Where are you going, my pret - ty maid, Where
4. "How old are you, my bon - nie lass, How

May morn - ing so ear - ly, I o - ver-took a
buck - les shone like sil - ver, She had a dark and
are you going, my hon - ey?" She an - swered me right
old are you my hon - ey?" She an - swered me right

bon - nie lass, And__ she was sing - ing clear - ly,
roll - ing eye, And her hair was on her shoul - der. With my
sau - ci - ly, "An__ er - rand for my mam - my."
cheer - ful - ly, "I'm__ sev - en - teen come Sun - day."

fal la lal, fal la lal, Fal lal lal lal la la.

5. I next went to her mammy's house
To woo her most sincerely,
And she came tripping down the stair
To welcome me most cheerly.

6. "Oh, lassie, will you marry me?
It must be now or never."
She flung herself into my arms
And said, "I'll love for ever."

Washington

NANCY BYRD TURNER

HOAGY CARMICHAEL

GIRLS

And

BOYS

He played by the riv-er when he was young;

raced with the rab-bits in the hills.

(Hum) _____ the hills. He fished for his min-nows, And

And hoot-ed back ___ at the whip-poor-wills. _____

climbed and swung, (Hum) _____ whip-poor-wills.

UNISON

Strong and slen-der and tall he grew, And then, one morn-ing the bu-gles blew,

O-ver the hills the sum-mons came, O-ver the riv - er's shin-ing rim,

rit.

He said the bu-gles called his name, Know-ing his coun-try need-ed him.

a tempo   SOLO   ALL, GIRLS

He an-swered, "I'm com-ing," and marched a-way For

many a night and many a day.———————

Boys

Tramp, tramp, tramp, tramp,

Perhaps when the marches were hot and long, He'd

Tramp, tramp, tramp, tramp, Tramp, tramp, tramp, tramp, Tramp, tramp, tramp, tramp,

think of the river floating by, Or, camping under the

Tramp, tramp, tramp, tramp, Tramp, tramp, tramp, tramp, Tramp, tramp, tramp, tramp,

winter sky, Would hear the whippoorwill's far-off song.———

Tramp, tramp, tramp, tramp, Tramp, tramp, tramp, tramp, Tramp, their song.———

Brave and loyal, in peace or strife, He loved America all his life.

The Marseillaise

Rouget de Lisle   Rouget de Lisle

Ye sons of France, a-wake to glo - ry! Hark, hark what myr-iads bid you
Al-lons, en - fants de la Pa - tri - e, Le jour de gloire est ar - ri -

rise! Your chil-dren, wives, and grand-sires___ hoar - y: Be-hold their
vé, Con - tre nous, de la ty - ran - ni - e, L'é - ten-

tears, and hear their ___ cries, Be-hold their tears, and___ hear their___
dard san-glant est le - vé, L'é - ten - dard___ san-glant est le-

cries! Shall hate-ful ty - rants mis - chief___ breed - ing, With hire-ling
vé. En - ten - dez - vous,___ dans les cam - pa - gnes, Mu -

hosts,— a ruf-fian— band, Af-fright and des-o-late the land,—
gir ces fé-ro-ces sol-dats? Ils vien-nent jus-que dans nos bras,—

While— peace and lib-er-ty lie bleed-ing? To arms,— to arms, ye
É-gor-ger— nos fils, nos com-pa-gnes! Aux ar - mes, Ci-toy-

brave, Th'a-veng - ing sword un-sheathe! March on, march on,
ens, For-mez— vos ba-tail-lons! Mar-chons, mar-chons,

all hearts re-solved On vic - to-ry or death!
Qu'un sang im-pur A-breu - ve nos sil-lons!

Vain Fancy

From the opera "The Magic Flute"
by Wolfgang Amadeus Mozart

First Voice

'Neath guid-ance of Fan-cy, We'll roam through the wide world, A-void-ing all
With Fan-cy as pi-lot, all trou-bles swift van-ish, The sun shines in

Second Voice

trou-bles as i-dle and vain; We'll sail o'er broad seas, in our fair-y boat
glo-ry and gold-en its beam; Air cas-tles we're build-ing and sor-rows we

row-ing, Nor heed the world and its bur-den of pain.
ban-ish, A-las, that pleas-ure is on-ly a dream.

First Voice

The winds soft-ly blow, the waves gen-tly flow; Hail, Fan-cy,
'Tis du-ty must sway, 'tis that we'll o-bey, For Fan-cy's

Second Voice

King of realms be-low, Hail, Fan-cy, King of realms be-low!
guid-ance leads us a-stray, For Fan-cy's guid-ance leads us a-stray.

O God, Our Help In Ages Past

HYMN TUNE: ST. ANNE
by W. CROFT

ISAAC WATTS

1. O God, our help in ag - es past, Our hope for years to come,
2. Un - der the shad - ow of Thy throne Thy saints have dwelt se - cure;

Our shel - ter from the storm - y blast And our e - ter - nal home.
Suf - fi - cient is Thine arm a - lone, And our de - fense is sure.

3. Before the hills in order stood,
   Or earth received her frame,
   From everlasting Thou art God,
   To endless years the same.

4. A thousand ages in Thy sight
   Are like an evening gone;
   Short as the watch that ends the night
   Before the rising sun.

5. Time, like an ever-rolling stream,
   Bears all its sons away;
   They fly, forgotten, as a dream
   Dies at the opening day.

6. O God, our help in ages past,
   Our hope for years to come,
   Be Thou our guide while life shall last,
   And our eternal home.

One of the most important requisites for fine singing is the ability to sustain the tones of a melody smoothly and evenly while pronouncing the words distinctly. The following is a splendid exercise for developing this skill. The phrases of O GOD, OUR HELP IN AGES PAST should be taken one at a time and sung on one pitch. The words are sung to this one tone, with clear articulation of each of the consonants, but without a break in the sustained tone. It is as though the words were floating on a smooth sea of tone. Then try singing the phrases, one at a time, with the correct melody, and with the same smoothness of tone and distinctness of speech.

O God, our help in ag-es past.   Our hope for years to come.

Phrases of other songs should be used in the same way, especially where there is some difficulty in singing the words distinctly. Other pitches should be used, sometimes high, sometimes low, in order to become accustomed to distinct articulation throughout the range of the voice.

Samoan Boat Song

Translation by
SEISI TOMINAGA

SAMOAN FOLK SONG
Adapted by MILDRED LOPER

With strongly marked rhythm

Come, let's go! All a-board, ev-'ry-bod-y, stead-y, boys, now row, Ev-'ry-
Le u - lae, le u - lae, o ma-i-a, o mai ta tou no, O mai

one now row! Come, let's go! Come, a-long with your ta-ro!
ta tou ou, Sei ta tou, Sei____ ta tou fa' lo - go

We are off for mar-ket, off for mar-ket we go. Ev-'ry-one o-beys the law.
i-u-pu la ma-lo, i-u-pu la ma-lo. O-lo u-a tau fa lo!

Carnival in Venice

Elizabeth Bennett

Italian Folk Song

1. Like earth-bound stars the lan-terns glow A-long ca-nal and street, And
2. Up-on a bridge stands Har-le-quin, Re-ject-ed and a-lone; The
3. A min-strel in a cloak of red Is fol-low-ing a song; A

from the gon-do-las drift-ing slow Come songs and laugh-ter sweet. In
qui-et wa-ters re-flect his twin, And si-lent as the stone. But
sau-cy gip-sy has tossed her head, And van-ished in the throng. Who

mer-ry mas-quer-ade Count and peas-ant, king, and clown, And
gen-tle Col-um-bine Comes to find her cho-sen one, And
is the mock-ing miss? None can guess who she may be, But

man-y a mis-chie-vous maid Goes a-danc-ing 'round the town.
then with their eyes__ a-shine, Off they rush to join the fun.
find her and steal__ a kiss; That will solve the mys-ter-y.

Invocation

ELEANOR ALLETTA CHAFFEE

FRANZ SCHUBERT

Ho - ly, ho - ly, ho - ly, heark - en to our
Ho - ly, ho - ly, ho - ly, when the night is
Hei - lig, hei - lig, hei - lig, hei - lig ist der

praise;_____ We who are Thy chil - dren
deep,_____ When the heart's low mu - sic
Herr!_____ Hei - lig, hei - lig, hei - lig;

of - fer Thee our days_____ That the light and beau-
pat - terns all our sleep,_____ Watch when we can watch
hei - lig ist nur Er!_____ All - macht, Wun - der, Lie-

ty of Thy gra - cious care_____ May be on our
not, wake when we are still,_____ And our emp - ty
be, al - les rings um - her,_____ Hei - lig, hei - lig,

path - way,   joy - ous   sun   to   share._____
dream - ing   with   Thy rich - ness fill._____
hei - lig,   hei - lig   ist   der   Herr._____

The third voice-part of this song should be sung by boys with rich low tones. The tones should be flowing and easy, but of a deep, smooth quality.

The Wind Among the Trees

FREDERICK H. MARTENS

WOLFGANG AMADEUS MOZART

The   for - est ev - er   ut - ters   A word - less mel - o-
It   is   a pleas - ant meas - ure Of hap - pi - ness and

dy,   That ev - 'ry sum - mer flut - ters   A-
ease,   That car - ries sum - mer's pleas - ure On

long__ from tree__ to   tree.   The wind, the wind is
gen - tle, sleep - y breeze.   A balm - y fra - grance

play - ing, And on the aft - er - noon,   There sounds thro' branch - es
bring - ing, How can it fail__ to please,   The song the wind is

stray - ing A hap - py lit - tle tune,_____ A___
sing - ing, The wind__ a - mong__ the trees,_____ The__

hap - py lit - tle tune,_____ A___ hap - py lit - tle tune.
wind a - mong the trees,_____ The __ wind a - mong the trees?

Land of Freedom

144

Paraphrased from the original Czech
by Nancy Byrd Turner

Traditional Czech Patriotic Song

Land of Free-dom, all thy sto-ry Ech-oes far a-round the world,
Land we love, thy moun-tains ev-er Stand about us staunch and strong;

Sounds forth to all the world. Oth-er na-tions mark thy glo-ry,
Stand guard-ing, high and strong; Through the mead-ows, stream and riv-er

Hail thy ra-diant flag un-furled, Splen-did, thy flag un-furled.
Sing of thee an end-less song, On-ward, an end-less song!

Man-y a land has watched thee far-ing Through the strife for free-dom dar-ing,
With thy beau-ty spread be-fore us, We, thy peo-ple, lift a cho-rus,

Seen their un-di-min-ished glo-ry Flame to the world!
Praise to-geth-er all thy cour-age Through the years long.

With the dawn thy prais-es wa-ken, val-or bright and

rit.   ' *Very Slowly*

will un - shak - en, Ring from moun-tain - top   to   shore, from moun-tain-

Slowly (religioso)

top   to   shore!   A - men! Straight and loy - al   we   will

I ONLY   I AND II

stand,   Read - y,   heart and   hand.   O, be - lov - ed

I-II-III

land,   Proud   to   serve   thee   ev - er - more!

Quickly

With   the dawn thy   prais - es   wak - en,   Val - or bright and

rit.

will   un - shak - en,   Ring   from moun - tain - top   to

' *Very Slowly*   4

shore, From moun - tain - top   to   shore!

The Spanish Cavalier
and
Solomon Levi

WILLIAM D. HENDRICKSON
and OLD COLLEGE SONG

A Span-ish Cav - a - lier   stood in   his re-treat,   And
And when the war   is .o'er,   'to   you   I'll re-turn,   A-

My name   is Sol-o-mon Le - vi; At__ my store on Sa - lem Street,__ That's
And if   a loaf - er comes a-long To my store on Sa - lem Street __ And.

on   his gui-tar   played a tune,   dear;   The
gain   to   my coun - try and you,   dear;   But

where you'll buy your coats and vests And ev-'ry-thing else that's neat;__ I've
tries   to hang me up   for coats And Vests__ so ver - y neat,_____ I

mu - sic   so sweet,   Would__ oft - times re - peat   The
if   I   be slain,   You may seek   me   in vain,   Up-

sec - ond-hand-ed ul - ster-ettes And ev - 'ry-thing that's fine.__ For__
kicks that loaf-er right out of my store And on him sets   my pup,__ For I

bless-ing of my coun - try and you,   dear.
on   the bat- tle - field __ you will   find   me.

all the boys, they trade with me, At a hun-dred and for-ty - nine.____
won't sell clothes to an - y man__ Who tries __ to hold me   up.____

Oh, Sol-o-mon Le - vi! Le - vi! tra la la la!___

Oh,

Poor Sol-o-mon Le - vi! Tra la la la la la la la la la,___ My

say, dar - ling, say, when I'm far a - way,

name is Sol-o-mon Le - vi; At my store on Sa - lem Street,___ That's

Some - times you may think of me, dear;

where you'll buy your coats and vests And ev-'ry-thing else that's neat;___ I've

Bright sun-ny days will soon fade a - way, Re-

sec - ond-hand-ed ul-ster-ettes and ev-'ry-thing else that's fine,___ For

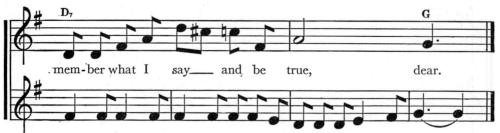

.mem-ber what I say___ and be true, dear.

all the boys they trade with me At a hun-dred and for - ty - nine.___

Parting

ELLEN WALES WALPOLE FOLK SONG from CHILE

Fare-well, now, my dar-ling, Smile through your sad tears, Sweet-ly smile for
take heart, my dear-est, Fare-well, my good friend, Sweet - ly smile for

me.___ Fare-well, now, my dar-ling, Qui-et your bad fears, Brave - ly smile for
me.___ So take heart, my dear-est, All part-ings must end, Gai - ly wave to

1. 2. Fine

me.___ So

me.___

A dark cloud scat-ter - ing rain-drops,___ With

sad - ness fills all the flow-ers;___ The rain may fall, but it

D.C. al Fine

then stops,___ And sun - shine fol - lows the show - ers.___

Prayer of Shipwrecked Men
or Great Ta-a-roa

Adapted from the TAHITIAN
by BERTA METZGER

HAWAIIAN SONG by
DOROTHY M. KAHANANUI

O - cean God, great Ta-a-roa, Calm___ the sea!

Cause the waves to lie out flat As the danc-ers' ha - la mat.

Grant, oh, grant that we may reach Wives and chil-dren on the beach.

O - cean God, great Ta-a-roa, Calm___ the sea!

La Tortue Naine
(*The Tiny Turtle*)

Translated from the FRENCH of
JACQUELINE KRIEGER by ELLEN WALES WALPOLE

DARIUS MILHAUD

On ne peut que trou-ver vi - lai - ne
Tell me, why do they so be - lit - tle,

U - ne per-son-ne vrai - ment nai - ne, Poum ne com - prend
Al - ways, why do they so be - lit - tle Ev - 'ry tee - ny,

pas pour quoi Pouic, sa tor - tue nai - ne, est ma
ti - ny one? My wee tur - tle, he is far more

foi Plus ad-mi-rée et moins ba-na - le Qu'u-ne gran-de bê-
fun, He can be far more cute and clev - er Than the big, full-grown

- te nor-ma - le.
_beast-ies ev - er.

Roundelay

W. Otto Miessner   W. Otto Miessner

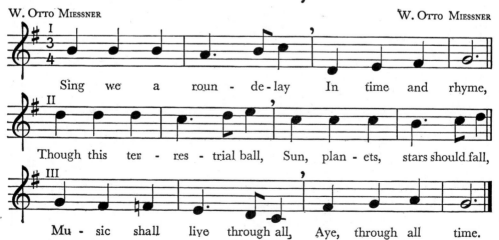

Sing we a roun - de-lay In time and rhyme,

Though this ter - res - trial ball, Sun, plan - ets, stars should fall,

Mu - sic shall live through all, Aye, through all time.

"Toy" Symphony

Franz Joseph Haydn

Haydn's celebrated "Toy" Symphony was written so that the family circle which made up
his audience in the country estate of his patron could amuse themselves by playing
along with the musicians. Only a few measures of the first movement are included here,
but they show how ingeniously Haydn brought in the simple toy instruments. They show
also how orchestra parts are written, and how the performer must learn to count
measures of rests and come in at the right time. After trying this brief portion of the
symphony, maybe you will get the complete work and take part in performing it.

Sailing

GODFREY MARKS

154

GODFREY MARKS

1. Y'heave ho!__ my lads,__ the wind blows free,__ A pleas - ant
2. The sail - or's life__ is bold and free,__ His home__ is
3. The tide__ is flow - ing with the gale,__ Y'heave ho!__ my

gale__ is on our lee;__ And soon__ a - cross__ the o - cean
on__ the roll - ing sea;__ And nev - er heart__ more true or
lads,__ set ev - 'ry sail;__ The har - bor bar__ we soon shall

clear,__ Our gal - lant bark__ shall brave - ly__ steer;__
brave,__ Than his__ who launch - es on__ the__ wave;__
clear;__ Fare-well,__ once more,__ to home__ so__ dear,__

But ere we part__ from Eng-land's shores to - night,__
A - far he speeds__ in dis - tant climes to roam,__
For when the tem - pest ra - ges loud and long,__

A song we'll sing__ for home and beau - ty bright.__
With joy - ous song__ he rides the spar-kling foam.__
That home shall be__ our guid-ing star and song.__

Then here's to the sail - or, and here's to the hearts__ so

rit.

true, Who will think of him up - on the wa - ter blue!__

On page 9, in explaining how to play chording accompaniments, you were shown the relationship of the treble and bass staves. It was there explained that the F Clef (𝄢)
is used to indicate the bass staff. In the refrain of SAILING you will observe that the
melody is printed on two staves, the tones represented being an octave apart. It may be
sung by the boys, who may read it from either the bass or the treble staff. Boys should
be familiar with the bass staff, because it will become increasingly useful as their voices
change into tenors and basses.

Swing Song

William Allingham

W. Otto Miessner

Swing, swing, sing, sing, Here__ my home__ and I am a
Up, down, up, down, Which is the way__ to Lon - don

king; Swing, swing, sing, sing, Fare - well, earth,__ for
Town? Here, there, up in the air, Close__your eyes__ and

I'm on the wing! Low, high, here__ I fly
now you are there! Soon, soon, aft - er - noon,

Like__ a bird through sun - ny sky; Free,_____
O - ver the sun - set, o - ver the moon; Far,_____

free,_____ o - ver the lea,_____ O - ver the
far,_____ o - ver all bar,_____ Sweep - ing

moun-tain and o - ver the sea!_____
on_____ from star_____ to star!_____

Coda

No,_____ no,_____ low,_____ Sweep - ing dai - sies

with__ my toe, Slow,_____ slow,_____ to and fro,

Slow,_____ slow,_____ slow._____

Men of the Air

ELEANOR GRAHAM

PHILIP JAMES

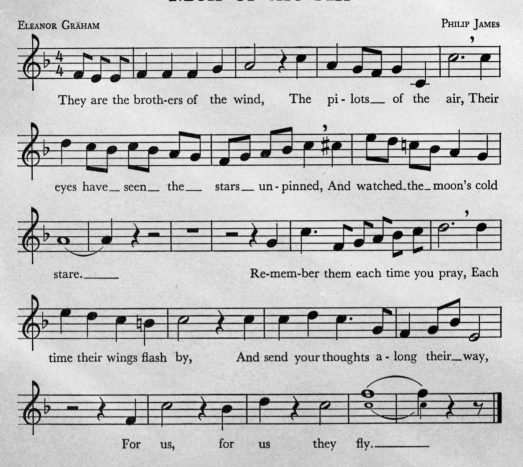

They are the broth-ers of the wind, The pi-lots— of the air, Their

eyes have— seen— the— stars— un-pinned, And watched_the_moon's cold

stare._____ Re-mem-ber them each time you pray, Each

time their wings flash by, And send your thoughts a-long their—way,

For us, for us they fly._____

Crusaders' Hymn

Anonymous, German, XVII Century

Old Silesian Folk Song

1. Fair - est Lord Je - sus, Rul - er of all na - ture,
2. Fair are the mead - ows, Fair - er still the wood - lands,
3. Fair is the sun - shine, Fair - er still the moon - light,

O Thou of God and man the Son;
Robed in the bloom - ing garb of spring;
And all the twin - kling, star - ry host;

Thee will I cher - ish, Thee will I hon - or,
Je - sus is fair - er, Je - sus is pur - er,
Je - sus shines bright - er, Je - sus shines pur - er,

Thou, my soul's glo - ry, joy, and crown.
Who makes the woe - ful heart to sing.
Than all the an - gels heav'n can boast.

From "CLAIR DE LUNE"
by CLAUDE DEBUSSY (1862-1918)

Andante très expressif

Permission granted by Jean Jobert, Paris, and Elkan-Vogel Co., Inc., Philadelphia, Pa., copyright owners.

From "GOLLIWOGG'S CAKE-WALK" by CLAUDE DEBUSSY

Allegro giusto

Permission granted by Durand & Cie, Paris, and Elkan-Vogel Co., Inc., Philadelphia, Pa., copyright owners.

Melody from "VALSE TRISTE" by JEAN SIBELIUS (1865—)

Lento espress.

Toward the close of the nineteenth century and in the early years of the twentieth century a new spirit showed itself in musical expression. A number of composers in various countries became dissatisfied with the more formal traditions of classical music. Wagner's operas had shown that the older system of harmony was capable of almost unlimited expansion. The younger composers began to experiment with newer kinds of melody, rhythm, and harmony. Although much of this experimental music is already forgotten, certain composers produced works in the new manner which continue to be performed and today are regarded as a part of our permanent musical literature. Among these composers, two are represented on this page, Debussy of France, and Sibelius of Finland. Both composers produced numerous works which were very different from the music of their predecessors and which became widely known and loved. Indeed, the three works from which themes are given are performed so often that they might well be considered as popular music, if we use the word "popular" to mean "familiar."

Debussy was the most important member of a group of French composers who aimed to express emotional impressions by means of music.

"Clair de lune" (moonlight), composed in 1890, is an early evidence of the style which later distinguished Debussy as a master in expressing atmospheric impressions.

In 1908 Debussy composed a humorous suite for his six-year old daughter, and called it "Children's Corner." The last movement, "Golliwogg's Cake-Walk," is in conscious imitation of American ragtime. A golliwogg is a rag doll, which explains the humor of this amusing exaggeration of the music for the Negro minstrel cake-walks of that period.

Sibelius' celebrated "Valse triste" has become so popular that with many people it has overshadowed his more important compositions. The word "triste" means "melancholy." The waltz, which tells a fantastic story of a departing soul, a sort of "dance of death," was written as part of the incidental music for a drama.

Git Along, Little Dogies!

As sung by
KATE TAYLOR PARMLEY

COWBOY SONG

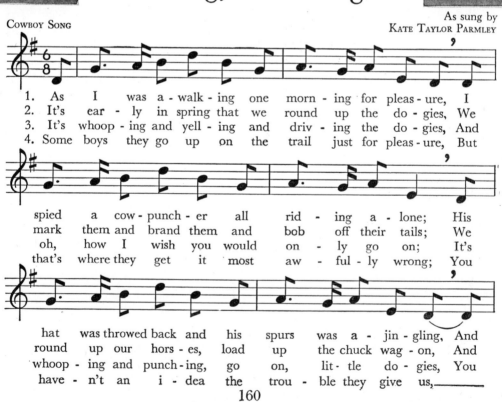

1. As I was a-walk-ing one morn-ing for pleas-ure, I
2. It's ear-ly in spring that we round up the do-gies, We
3. It's whoop-ing and yell-ing and driv-ing the do-gies, And
4. Some boys they go up on the trail just for pleas-ure, But

spied a cow-punch-er all rid-ing a-lone; His
mark them and brand them and bob off their tails; We
oh, how I wish you would on-ly go on; It's
that's where they get it most aw-ful-ly wrong; You

hat was throwed back and his spurs was a-jin-gling, And
round up our hors-es, load up the chuck wag-on, And
whoop-ing and punch-ing, go on, lit-tle do-gies, You
have-n't an i-dea the trou-ble they give us,_____

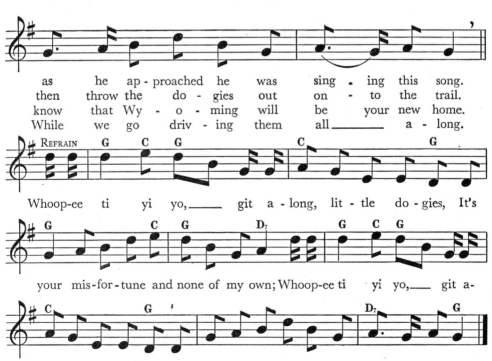

as   he ap - proached he   was   sing . ing this   song.
then   throw the   do - gies   out   on - to the   trail.
know   that Wy - o - ming will   be   your new home.
While   we   go   driv - ing them   all_____   a - long.

Whoop-ee ti   yi   yo,_____ git a - long, lit - tle do - gies, It's

your mis-for-tune and none of my own; Whoop-ee ti   yi yo,_____ git a-

long, lit - tle do-gies, You know that Wy - o-ming will   be your new home.

Rain

Annie Willis McCullough

Paul Hindemith

The spring rain helps the bush - es bud A-

Moderato

long the gar - den path; The sum-mer rain gives

dust - y leaves A most re-fresh - ing bath; The

fall rain pelts the chest-nuts down Up - on the ground be-

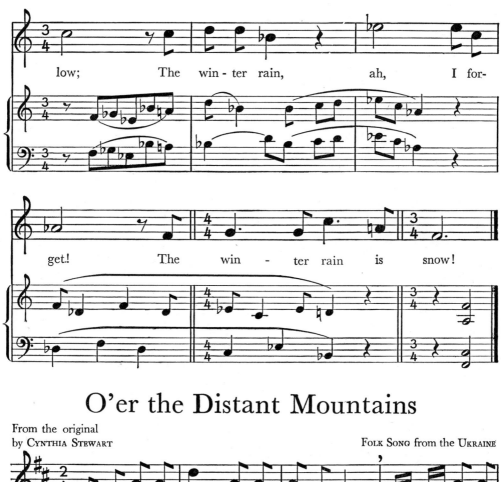

low; The win-ter rain, ah, I for-

get! The win - ter rain is snow!

O'er the Distant Mountains

From the original
by CYNTHIA STEWART

FOLK SONG from the UKRAINE

1. O'er the dis-tant moun - tains I wan-der on, O'er_ the_ dis-tant
2. Wealth and fame shall ne'er make my steps to roam, Wealth_and_fame shall
3. Swift-ly, then, I come, oh my dear-est one, Swift-ly,_then, I

moun - tains I wan-der on, Seek - ing for my loved_ one; where
ne'er make my steps to roam Till I find my loved_ one and
come, oh my dear-est one; I shall hold you fast_ when the

has she gone? Seek - ing for my loved_ one; where has she gone?
bring her home; Till I find my loved_ one and bring her home.
search is done; I shall hold you fast_ when the search is done!

Polonaise

DANCE DIRECTIONS

Formation: Couples, dancers standing side by side with inside hands joined at shoulder height.

Figure: On count one, take a short step forward on inside foot, at the same time raising outside foot diagonally forward. Bend body slightly toward raised foot. This step is sometimes taken as a small jump. The outside arm swings out and in alternately, as outside and inside feet are raised. On counts two and three, step forward two steps, outside foot first.

Alternate the entire step continuously. The dance is dignified, and may be either stately or vigorous. A leading couple takes the group through a floor pattern which (1) starts in a circle completely around the room; (2) comes down center of room; (3) couples alternate right and left up sides of room, passing each other and going down opposite side of room; (4) go diagonally forward from back corner of room to front corner with couples passing alternately in center of room. First couples form an arch through which other couples pass. Other floor patterns can be formed.

In Days of Old

MARY BUDLONG   FRENCH FOLK SONG

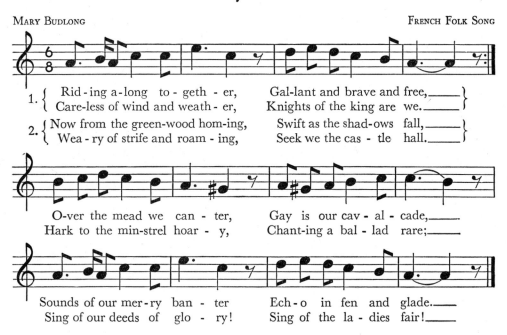

1. { Rid-ing a-long to-geth - er,   Gal-lant and brave and free,_____ }
    Care-less of wind and weath - er,   Knights of the king are we._____

2. { Now from the green-wood hom-ing,   Swift as the shad-ows fall,_____ }
    Wea - ry of strife and roam - ing,   Seek we the cas - tle hall._____

O-ver the mead we can - ter,   Gay is our cav - al - cade,_____
Hark to the min-strel hoar - y,   Chant-ing a bal - lad rare;_____

Sounds of our mer-ry ban - ter   Ech-o in fen and glade.___
Sing of our deeds of glo - ry!   Sing of the la - dies fair!___

Nightingale Song

KARL ZELLER, 1898

SOLO or SEMI-CHORUS

When my sire was twen-ty years,____ And a hun-ter with-out
Years have passed since first they met,____ But their hearts are hap-py

fears,__'Neath the moon-light,full of joy____ He first saw his Re-si
yet,____ In each oth-er they have found__Peace and hap-pi-ness a-

coy. As he met her in the vale__They could hear a night-in-
bound. In their cot-tage in the vale__They can hear the night-in-

gale.____ Now these two in their de-light Oft wished by day and
gale;____ And these two in their de-light Still wish by day and

night:_____ REFRAIN Sing a-gain, sing a-gain,night-in-gale,__That sweet
night:_____

strain,_sing a-gain,__ Sing a-gain, sing a-gain,night-in-gale,__ As thou

CHORUS

sang-est in__ the vale.____ Sing a-gain, sing a-gain, night-in-

gale,_____ That sweet strain,_____ sing a - gain,_____ Sing a-

Sing a- gain, that sweet strain, Sing a-gain, Sing a-

gain, sing a-gain, night-in-gale,_____ As thou sang-est in the vale._____

gain, sing a-gain, night-in-gale, night-in-gale, In the vale._____

Praise the Lord
(*Adir Hu*)

Paraphrased from the Psalms · TRADITIONAL HEBREW MELODY

Moderately fast

Praise the Lord! One ac - cord, Sound through-out cre - a - tion.
Lo! The spring joy doth bring; Win - ter's frosts are__ end - ed.
A - dir hu A - dir hu Yiv - neh vey - so b' - ko - rov

Laud and sing,_____ hon - or bring Him with-out ces - sa - tion,
Glad-ness reigns,_____ life re-mains With sweet pleas-ure blend - ed.
Bim - hey - roh_____ bim - hey - roh B'yo-mey - nu b' - ko - rov.

And His fame loud pro-claim Ev -'ry land and na - tion.
God doth bear what His care And His love de - fend - ed.
Eyl b' - ney Eyl b' - ney b'ney veys - cho b' - ko - rov.

Ah, Lovely Meadows

(*Aj, lúčka, lúčka široká*)

Translated from the CZECH

CZECH FOLK SONG

In March Tempo. *Two swings to a measure*

1. Ah, love-ly mead-ows, green and wide, Grass-es are grow-ing, grass-es are
2. Loud-ly the bar-on blows his horn, Wake up, my stew-ard, wake up, my
3. Har-ness your horse, the hours are few, Work-ing to-geth-er, work-ing to-

Aj, lúč-ka, lúč-ka ši-ro-ká, ros-te na ní trá-va, ros-te na ní

grow-ing, Ah, love-ly mead-ows, green and wide, Grow-ing_ so high on
stew-ard, Reap-ing be-gins at ear-ly morn, Wake up,_my stew-ard,
geth-er, Off to the fields of gold-en hue, Gath-er_the grain ere
trá-va. Aj, lúč-ka, lúč-ka ši-ro-ká, ros-te_na ní trá-va

CHORUS

ev-'ry side. (Hey!)
day is born. Wa-ter from moun-tain flows, Melt-ed from win-ter snows,
falls the dew. *Te-če vo-da z ho-ra, čis-tá je ja-ko já,*
vy-so-ká. (Hej!)

Turn-ing, it gai-ly goes, Cir-cling the ma-ple tree, Wa-ter from moun-tain flows,
to-čí se do ko-la, o-ko-lo ja-vo-ra; te-če vo-da z ho-ra,

Melt-ed from win-ter snows, Turn-ing, it gai-ly goes, Call-ing to me. (Hey!)
čis-tá je ja-ko já, to-čí se do ko-la, o-ko-lo mňa. (Hej!)

The Mountain Stream

Translated by
CYNTHIA STEWART

ERNST SIMON
from the TYROLEAN ALPS

Down the moun-tain-side Doth a stream-let glide,
Where the wa-ter sweeps And the cham-ois leaps,

YODEL

Hul - da - e hul - di - o - i du - i - da.

In a sun-ny spot Stands a lit-tle cot,
Where the sweet birds sing, There my yo-dels ring,

YODEL

Hul - di - e hul - di - o - i du - i - da.

In the gar-den there Sits a la-dy fair,
'Mid the fresh-et green, Al - pine flow'rs are seen,

YODEL

Hul - di - e juch - a juch - a juch - a hul - di - e.

As I pass a - long She can hear my song,
In her cot-tage there Dwells my la - dy fair,

YODEL

Hul - di - e juch - a juch - a juch - a he!

The Cuckoo

From the original Czech
by Jane Rolfe Randolph

Czech Folk Song

Tell me, lit-tle cuck-oo, if you can, sir, Tell me where you've
What a fun-ny way to give an an-swer; Can't you make your

been all year. Cuck-oo! Cuck-oo! Cuck-oo, cuck-oo, cuck-oo!
mean-ing clear? Cuck-oo! Cuck-oo! Cuck-oo, cuck-oo, cuck-oo!

Cuck-oo, cuck-oo, cuck-oo! Cuck-oo!

Sixteenth Notes

The rhythm of four sixteenth notes to a beat can be learned by speaking (scanning) the words of the first measure of THE CUCKOO while beating the time. Then apply the rhythm in reading a new song.

Beats: 1   2

Tell me, lit-tle cuck-oo,

My Lovely Maiden

Elizabeth Bennett

Folk Tune from Lapland

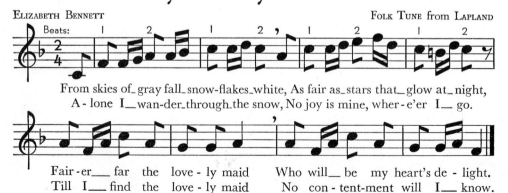

From skies of_gray fall_snow-flakes_white, As fair as_stars that_glow at_night,
A-lone I_wan-der_through_the snow, No joy is mine, wher-e'er I_go.

Fair-er__ far the love-ly maid Who will__ be my heart's de-light.
Till I__ find the love-ly maid No con-tent-ment will I__ know.

A Village Dance

Elizabeth Bennett

Folk Song from Yugoslavia

1. Come and join the mer - ry - mak-ing, Tra la la la!____
2. Now the fid - dles gai - ly__ sound-ing, Tra la la la,____
3. Sum - mer is the time for__ danc-ing, Tra la la la,____

Hear the tam-bou - rine a - shak-ing, Tra la la la.____
Set our hap-py hearts a - bound-ing, Tra la la la.____
Youth the sea-son for ro - manc-ing, Tra la la la.____

Choose a____ part-ner, ev - 'ry-one, Join the__ dance and share the fun;
Left and__right, and in and out, Whirl and__ twirl and turn a - bout,
So be - fore the sum-mer ends, Make the__ most of time and friends,

Tap and__snap to tunes so gay On our__ vil - lage hol - i - day.
Danc-ing__ on the vil-lage green To the__mer - ry tam-bou-rine.
And though_Age will come some day, Hearts will__ still be light and gay.

Which Shall It Be?

JANE ROLFE RANDOLPH

CZECH FOLK SONG

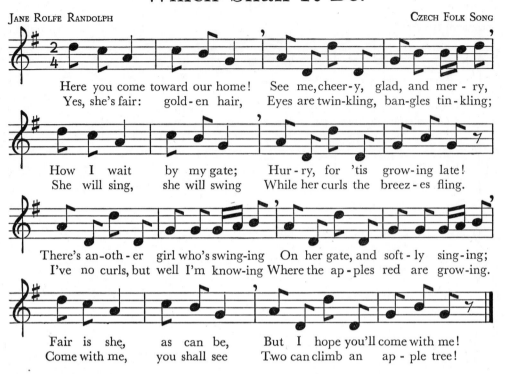

Here you come toward our home! See me, cheer-y, glad, and mer-ry,
Yes, she's fair: gold-en hair, Eyes are twin-kling, ban-gles tin-kling;

How I wait by my gate; Hur-ry, for 'tis grow-ing late!
She will sing, she will swing While her curls the breez-es fling.

There's an-oth-er girl who's swing-ing On her gate, and soft-ly sing-ing;
I've no curls, but well I'm know-ing Where the ap-ples red are grow-ing.

Fair is she, as can be, But I hope you'll come with me!
Come with me, you shall see Two can climb an ap-ple tree!

Haydn was born in a little village a few miles east of Vienna, near the Czech border. Here he undoubtedly heard many Czech folk songs which remained in his memory. He used the melody of this song, WHICH SHALL IT BE? in the last movement of his well-known Symphony in D, often called the the "London" Symphony.

Black-eyed Susie

TRADITIONAL

AMERICAN FOLK SONG

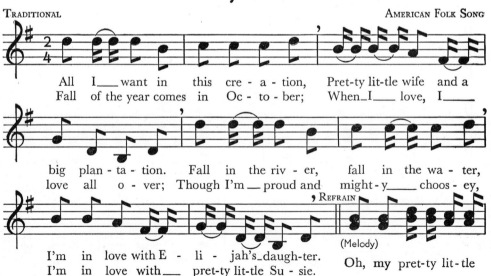

All I ___ want in this cre-a-tion, Pret-ty lit-tle wife and a
Fall of the year comes in Oc-to-ber; When ___ I ___ love, I ___

big plan-ta-tion. Fall in the riv-er, fall in the wa-ter,
love all o-ver; Though I'm ___ proud and might-y ___ choos-ey,

, REFRAIN

I'm in love with E-li-jah's ___ daugh-ter.
I'm in love with ___ pret-ty lit-tle Su-sie.

(Melody)

Oh, my pret-ty lit-tle

black-eyed Su - sie, Oh, my pret-ty lit-tle black-eyed Su - sie,

Oh, my pret-ty lit-tle black-eyed Su-sie, Oh, my pret-ty lit-tle Sue.

Fiesta

Paraphrased from the original by
MARY BUDLONG

FOLK SONG from MEXICO

(All) 1–3. A light gui - tar   in the dusk soft-ly strum-ming,__From near and
                     sweet se - ño - ri - ta I'm danc-ing,___   A red, red

far   now the danc - ers are com-ing.____ The gold-en lan - terns a-
rose   in her hair, how en-tranc-ing!____ And in her heart,   as we're

bove   us are swing-ing,____ And on the soft eve-ning air voic-es
glid - ing and sway-ing,____ I fond-ly hope sweet Chi-qui - ta will

ring, tra la la la! (Boys) We'll do a lit-tle dance to - geth-er,
say,   tra la. la la! (Girls) We'll do a lit-tle dance to - geth-er,

Chi - qui-ta is the one for me! We'll do a lit-tle dance to-
Pe - ri-co is the one for me! We'll do a lit-tle dance to-

geth - er, Chi - qui - ta is the one for me! 2. Now with a
geth - er, Pe - ri-co is the one for me! 3. A light gui-

Prelude to Spring

MARY BUDLONG

MIKAEL NYBERG
FINNISH COMPOSER

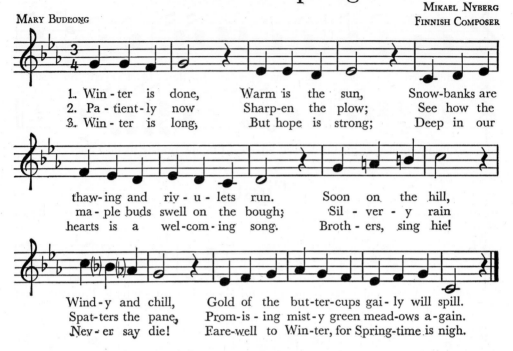

1. Win-ter is done,   Warm is the sun,   Snow-banks are
2. Pa-tient-ly now   Sharp-en the plow;   See how the
3. Win-ter is long,   But hope is strong;   Deep in our

thaw-ing and riv-u-lets run.   Soon on the hill,
ma-ple buds swell on the bough;   Sil-ver-y rain
hearts is a wel-com-ing song.   Broth-ers, sing hie!

Wind-y and chill,   Gold of the but-ter-cups gai-ly will spill.
Spat-ters the pane,   Prom-is-ing mist-y green mead-ows a-gain.
Nev-er say die!   Fare-well to Win-ter, for Spring-time is nigh.

A Message

MARTHA DABNEY

FOLK SONG from LATVIA

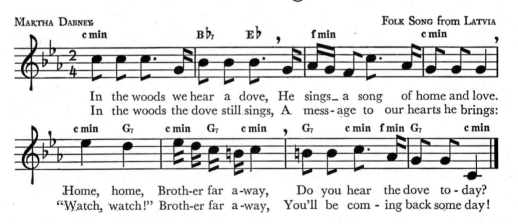

In the woods we hear a dove, He sings a song of home and love.
In the woods the dove still sings, A mess-age to our hearts he brings:

Home, home, Broth-er far a-way,   Do you hear the dove to-day?
"Watch, watch!" Broth-er far a-way,   You'll be com-ing back some day!

Chording in the Key of C Minor

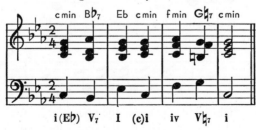

i(Eb)   V₇   I   (c)i   iv   V♮₇   i

MAJOR AND TONIC (PARALLEL) MINOR SCALES

The Major and Minor Scales are arranged above in tetrachords so that their like-nesses and differences may be clearly seen. A tetrachord is a series of four tones. You will observe that the lower tetrachord is the same in all three forms of the minor scale, Normal, Harmonic, and Melodic. It is in the upper tetrachord that differences will be found. You have already studied the way that the Normal and Harmonic Minor Scales are built. In the Melodic Minor Scale the upper tetrachord has one form when ascend-ing and another form when descending. The ascending upper tetrachord of this scale has the same intervals as the ascending upper tetrachord of the major scale. The descending upper tetrachord of the Melodic Minor Scale has the same intervals as the descending upper tetrachord of the Normal Minor Scale. The reason why we use the Melodic form of the minor scale is that it gives a smoother and simpler flow to the melody line and avoids the harsh and awkward step-and-a-half interval from 6 to 7 as found in the Harmonic Minor Scale. This use of the Melodic Minor Scale is beauti-fully shown in measures 9 to 12 of the song, PRELUDE TO SPRING, by the distinguished Finnish composer, Mikael Nyberg.

Teach Us to Worship Thee
(*Et Incarnatus Est*)

ELEANOR ALLETTA CHAFFEE

FRANZ JOSEPH HAYDN
From Mass in B-flat

Et in - car - na - tus est de ___ Spir - i - tu San - cto
Teach us to wor-ship Thee, Thy ___ glo - ry and ma-jes-ty;

Ex Ma - ri - a, Ma - ri - a ___ Vir - gi - ne.
Help - less, turn ___ we no - where ___ but ___ un - to Thee.

Et in - car - na - tus est de ___ Spir - i - tu San - cto
Teach us hu - mil - i - ty And ___ grant us the gift to see

Ex ___ Ma - ri - a, Ma - ri - a ___ Vir - gi - ne.
Love's ___ own grace and mer - cy ___ for ___ such as ___ we.

Et ho - mo fa - ctus est, et ___ ho - mo fa - ctus est,
Guide us that we may be For - ev - er near to Thee,

Et_____ ho - mo,___ et ho - mo fa - ctus est.
Ho - ly Fa - ther,___ Thy chil - dren pray to Thee.

Rowing Song

Translated from the GERMAN
by NANCY BYRD TURNER

JOHANNES BRAHMS

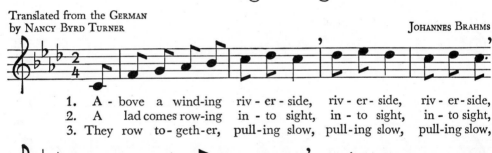

1. A - bove a wind-ing riv-er-side, riv-er-side, riv-er-side,
2. A lad comes row-ing in - to sight, in - to sight, in - to sight,
3. They row to-geth-er, pull-ing slow, pull-ing slow, pull-ing slow,

A maid-en at her win-dow stands, her win - dow wide. The__
His oars are dip-ping in the stream, the stream so bright. He__
They pull to-geth - er, keep-ing time, as on they go; Then__

riv - er shines from shore to shore, She lis-tens for a dip-ping oar,
sees her at the win-dow tall, "Come take an oar," she hears him call,
drift be-tween the qui-et shores With rain-bows drip-ping from their oars,

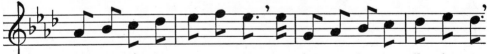

The sil - ver sound of dip-ping oar a - cross the tide.
And laugh-ing down the steps she runs, with foot-steps light.
And sing a' song of long a - go, of long a - go.

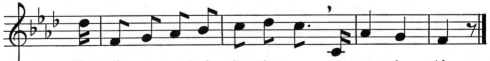

Waiting

Paraphrased from the Russian
by Elizabeth Bennett

From the opera "Khovantschina"
by Modest Mussorgsky

1. Wax-en can-dles bright-ly burn-ing Show a pret - ty___ maid in tears.
2. Ev - er - more her heart is yearn-ing For her sol - dier___ far a - way.
3. Home-ward then the lad, re-turn-ing, Finds the can - dles___ flam-ing high.

Oh, Oh! Who can know What the lone - ly___ maid - en fears?
"Oh, Oh! Can-dles glow! Bring him back__to__ me some day."
"Oh, Oh! Fate will show Love like ours__will__ nev - er die."

Homeland

Ellen Wales Walpole

Folk Song from Russia

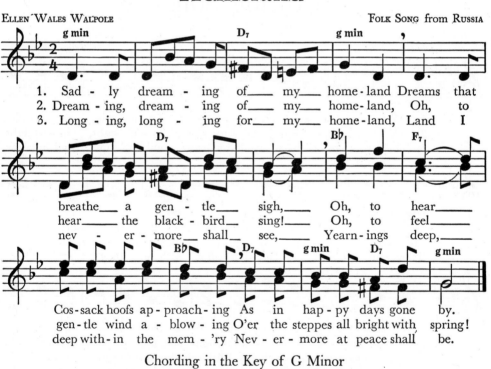

1. Sad - ly dream - ing of___ my___ home - land Dreams that
2. Dream - ing, dream - ing of___ my___ home - land, Oh, to
3. Long - ing, long - ing for___ my___ home - land, Land I

breathe___ a gen - tle___ sigh,___ Oh, to hear___
hear___ the black - bird__ sing!___ Oh, to feel___
nev - er - more__ shall__ see,___ Yearn - ings deep,___

Cos-sack hoofs ap - proach - ing As in hap - py days gone by.
gen - tle wind a - blow - ing O'er the steppes all bright with spring!
deep with - in the mem - 'ry Nev - er - more at peace shall be.

Chording in the Key of G Minor

i   V#7   i (Bb)V7   I (g)V#7   i

God Is Our Song

NANCY BYRD TURNER

LUDWIG VAN BEETHOVEN

1. The Lord is great, and great His end - less glo - ry;
2. The Lord is kind, His watch - ful love up - holds us,
3. The Lord is near, a change-less Friend and Giv - er,

Earth and the skies pro - claim His won-drous sto - ry; He
All through our life His faith - ful-ness en - folds us; The
His chil-dren know He will be with them ev - er. He

shines up - on the deep - est night, No
road is safe when by His side; We
gives us joy, He makes us strong. Our

dark - ness there, for God is Light.
can - not stray, with God for guide.
strength is God, and God our song!

The Soft-Shell Crab

Elsie J. Cooley

George W. Chadwick

There was a soft-shell crab, A ver-y, ver-y queer young
One day he went a-way; They looked in all the

fel-low, In col-or pink and drab, All spot-ted in with
plac-es Where once he used to play, Then said with sol-emn

yel-low, Who deep-ly shocked his dear ma-ma, His un-cles and his
fac-es, "This child to some sad end has come, A soup, stew, or a-

grand-pa-pa, His aunts se-date, his cous-ins eight, (To be played on an in-
qua-ri-um; 'Tis an aw-ful fate to be cooked and ate. strument or whistled.)

Be-cause he would walk for-ward straight.
But you see what comes of his walk-ing straight."

Old Folks At Home—Humoresque

Stephen C. Foster

Stephen C. Foster—Antonin Dvořák

Violin obbligato (or humming)

'Way down up-on the Swa-nee riv-er,
All up and down the whole cre-a-tion,

Far, far a-way, There's where my heart is
Sad-ly I roam, Still long-ing for the

turn - ing ev - er, There's where the old folks___ stay;
old plan - ta-tion, And for the old folks at home.

All the world is sad and drear-y, ev - 'ry-where I roam;

8va ad lib.

Oh, broth-ers, how my heart grows wea-ry,

Far from the old folks at home!

Listen to the Mockingbird

ALICE HAWTHORNE

1. I'm dream-ing now of___ Hal-lie,___ sweet__ Hal-lie,___
2. Ah! well I yet re - mem-ber,___ re - mem-ber,___
3. When charms of spring a - wak-en,___ a - wak-en,___

sweet__ Hal-lie,___ I'm dream-ing now of___ Hal-lie,___
re - mem-ber,___ Ah! well I yet re - mem-ber___
a - wak-en,___ When charms of spring a - wak-en,___

For the thought of her is one that nev - er dies;___ She's
When we gath-ered in the cot - ton, side by side;___ 'Twas
And the mock-ing-bird is sing - ing on the bough,___ I

sleep - ing now in the val - ley,___ the___ val - ley,___ the___
in the mild Sep - tem - ber,___ Sep - tem - ber,___ Sep -
feel like one for - sak - en,___ for - sak - en,___ for -

val - ley,___ She's sleep - ing now in the val - ley,___ And the
tem - ber,___ 'Twas in the mild Sep - tem - ber,___ And the
sak - en,___ I feel like one for - sak - en,___ Since my

CHORUS

mock-ing-bird is sing-ing where she lies. ___
mock-ing-bird was sing-ing far and wide.___ Lis-ten to the mock-ing-bird,
Hal-lie is no long-er with me now.___

Lis-ten to the mock-ing-bird, The mock-ing-bird is sing-ing o'er her

This universally beloved old song is splendid for spontaneous part singing. Some pupils carry the melody while others fill in the harmony, each one taking the part he prefers. Be sure your voice blends well with the other voices.

grave; Lis-ten to the mock-ing-bird, Lis-ten to the

mock-ing-bird, Still sing-ing where the weep-ing wil-lows wave.___

Charlie Is My Darling

LADY NAIRNE

TRADITIONAL SCOTTISH TUNE

Oh, Char - lie is my dar - ling, my dar - ling, my dar - ling!

Char - lie is my dar - ling, the young Che - va - lier!

1. 'Twas on a Mon-day morn - ing, Right ear - ly in the year, That
2. As he came march-in' up the street, The pipes played loud and clear, And
3. Wi' Hie - land bon-nets on their heads, And clay-mores bright and clear, They

D.S. %: al Fine

Char - lie came to our ___ town, The ___ young ___ Che - va - lier. Oh,
a' the folks came run-nin' out To ___ meet the Che - va - lier. Oh,
cam to fight for Scot-land's right, And the young ___ Che - va - lier. Oh,

Deck Thyself, My Soul

From the German of
Johann Franck (1649)

Johann Crüger (1649)
Harmonized by Johann Sebastian Bach

Deck thy-self, my soul, with glad - ness, Leave the gloom-y haunts of sad - ness; Come in - to the day-light's splen - dor, There with joy Thy prais - es ren - der Un - to Him whose grace un - bound - ed Hath this glo - rious ban - quet found - ed. High o'er all the heav'ns He reign - eth,

Yet to dwell with__ thee__ He deign - eth.

Homesick

From the original RUSSIAN by
JANE ROLFE RANDOLPH

RUSSIAN FOLK SONG

1. All is dark and__ cold In the for - est deep_ and_
2. I re - call a__ land Where the trees in beau - ty_
3. Gloom-y woods, fare - well! There's a call that's like_ a_

old; Snow on ev - 'ry bough, Si-lence far and near;
stand; Skies are bright and blue, Wa-ters gen - tly flow.
bell. One who wan - ders long Should not al - ways roam;

Win - ter falls, and now Life is lone - ly here.
'Tis a land I knew Long and long a - go.
With an an - sw'ring song I am go - ing home!

A Boating Song

REBECCA B. FORESMAN

WOLFGANG AMADEUS MOZART

With the love - ly moon a - bove us We__ are glid - ing free_from care
There is noth - ing to af - fright us As__ we calm - ly glide_a - long;

On the stream with scarce a rip - ple, Gen - tly float - ing
From the wil - lows comes a whis - per Like__ a maid - en's

here_and there. Swing-ing soft - ly, drift - ing i - dly, Glides our boat a -
eve - ning song. Let us heed no dream - y voic - es Call - ing on - ward

long__ the way, While the wa - ter, gen - tly swell - ing, Toss - es her_ as
to__ the sea, Tell - ing of the gold - en treas - ures Hid - den there.for

if____ in play, Toss - es__ her____ as if____ in play.
you__ and me, Hid - den_there__ for you__ and me.

Cradle Song

CLAUDIUS

FRANZ SCHUBERT

1. Slum - ber, slum - ber, ten - der lit - tle__ flow - er,
2. Slum - ber, slum - ber, lit - tle fad - ed__ flow - er,
3. Slum - ber, slum - ber, lit - tle an - gel__ flow - er,

Moth-er's lov-ing care doth a - round_thee_twine; Sweet and rest - ful
Still doth moth - er's love a - round_thee_glow; Strong-er is____ it
Though thou li - est 'neath the moss - y __ sod, Thou shalt wake_ in

be____ this hour,_ Sooth-ing fall__ this lul - la - by__ of__ mine.
than_death's pow-er, Guard-ing thee_wher - e'er thy spir - it__ go.
ros - y bow-er; Ros - es grow__ a - round the throne_of__ God.

Napoli

Nixon Waterman

Luigi Caracciolo

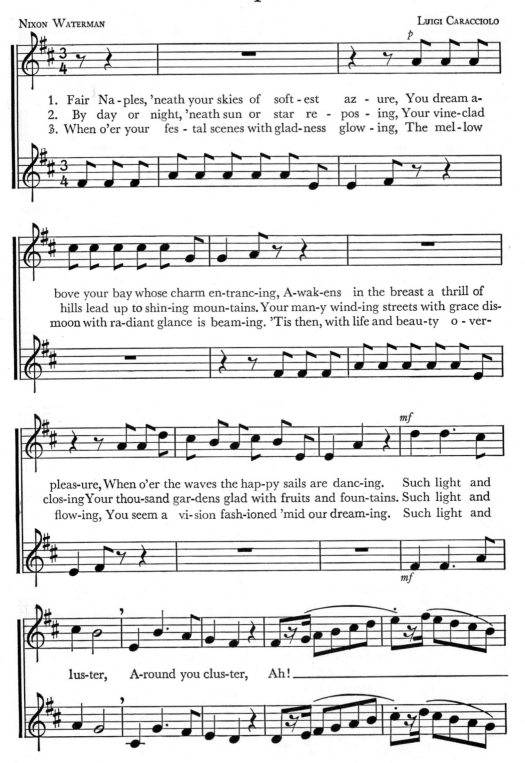

1. Fair Na-ples, 'neath your skies of soft-est az-ure, You dream a-
2. By day or night, 'neath sun or star re-pos-ing, Your vine-clad
3. When o'er your fes-tal scenes with glad-ness glow-ing, The mel-low

bove your bay whose charm en-tranc-ing, A-wak-ens in the breast a thrill of
hills lead up to shin-ing moun-tains. Your man-y wind-ing streets with grace dis-
moon with ra-diant glance is beam-ing. 'Tis then, with life and beau-ty o-ver-

pleas-ure, When o'er the waves the hap-py sails are danc-ing. Such light and
clos-ing Your thou-sand gar-dens glad with fruits and foun-tains. Such light and
flow-ing, You seem a vi-sion fash-ioned 'mid our dream-ing. Such light and

lus-ter, A-round you clus-ter, Ah! ____

Your charms are rar-est, rar -

est, Of cit-ies you___ are___ fair - est.

This delightful song of sunny Italy offers a splendid opportunity for contrasting vocal styles. The opening section of the song is a sort of intoned speech. Then comes a phrase for two voices in which the tones must be well sustained and blended. In the gay phrase sung to "ah," the tones should be tossed off with sparkling brightness. This phrase offers a fine experience in vocal flexibility.

Polish Patriotic Hymn

ELIZABETH BENNETT

PATRIOTIC HYMN from POLAND

Great is the glo - ry, proud is the sto - ry,
Schol - ars and writ - ers, states - men and fight - ers,
Z dy - mem po - ża - rów, z ku - rzem krwi brat - niej
Skar - ga to ostra ożna, jęk to os - tat - ni

Cra - dle of free - dom, my na - tive land!
Pride of our coun - try, stead - fast to stand.
Do Cie - bie, Pa - nie, wo - ła - ten głos
Od ta - kich mod - litw bie - le - je włos

Pa - tient in griev - ing, hope still be - liev - ing,
My już bez pła - czu, nie zna - my śpie - wu,

Strong with the strength of souls that are free;
Wie - niec cier - nio - wy wrósł w na - szą okroń.

True ven - er - a - tion give we our na - tion,
Wiecz - nie jak pom - nik Two - je - go gnie - wu

Loy - al for - ev - er, Po - land, to thee.
Ster - czy ku To - bie bła - gal - na dloń

Gathering Peascods

Violin (or singing with "la la")

OLD ENGLISH DANCE TUNE

REFRAIN

1. Four couples join hands in a circle. Slide eight slides to right. Turn single (drop hands and turn around with four running steps). Take hands and slide eight slides to left. Turn single.
Refrain: The girls go in center, join hands and slide around to right in a circle, returning to places at end of twelve counts. Boys repeat. *Girls walk toward center of circle with three steps. Clap own hands together a little higher than shoulder height on count 3. Bring feet together on count 4. As girls start walking back to places with four steps, the boys come forward to center of circle, clapping hands on count 3. As boys start back, the girls go in, returning to places with a turn single, while the boys remain in place. Repeat from *, but with the boys walking toward center first, then girls.
2. "Siding" — couples face in single circle and change places with walking step in four counts passing left shoulders. Return to place in four counts passing right shoulders. Turn single. Repeat. Refrain.
3. "Arming" — couples face, link right arms and run around each other in 8 counts. Drop arms and turn single. Repeat, linking left arms. Turn single. Refrain.
Finish with bow to partner as the music slows up.

The Owl and the Pussycat

Edward Lear   George Ingraham

1. The__ owl and the pus-sy-cat went__to sea in a beau-ti-ful pea-green boat;
2. Pus-sy said to the owl, "You el-e-gant fowl, how__charm-ing-ly sweet you sing!

They took__some hon-ey and plen-ty of mon-ey Wrapped up in a five-pound__note.
Oh, let us be mar-ried, too long we have tar-ried; But what shall we do for a ring?"

The owl looked up to the stars a - bove, And __ sang to a small gui - tar:
They sailed a - way for a year and a day To the land where the bong-tree grows.

CHORUS
"O love - ly Pus - sy, O Pus-sy, my love, __ what a
And there in a wood, __ a pig-gy - wig stood, __ with a

beau-ti - ful____ pus - sy you are!"_____
ring____ at the end of his nose._____

3. "Dear Pig, are you will-ing to sell for a shil-ling your ring?"

Said the pig-gy, "I will." So they took it a-way and were

mar-ried next day By the tur-key that lives on the hill. They

dined on mince and slic-es of quince, Which they ate with a run-ci-ble spoon;

And hand in hand, on the edge of the sand, They

danced by the light of the moon.

194 Young Man Who Wouldn't Hoe Corn

TRADITIONAL

MARSHALL BARTHOLOMEW

1. I'll sing you a song, and it's not____ ver - y long, It's a-
2. plant-ed his corn in the month__ of____ June, And____
4. So he____ went down to his neigh - bor's door, Where__
5. "Here__ you are a - want-in'__ for to wed, And__

bout a young man who would-n't hoe__ corn; The rea - son__why I____
(2) in____ Ju - ly it was__ knee - high: First of Sep - tem - ber__
(4) he____ had of - ten been__ be - fore; "Pret-ty lit-tle miss, will you
(5) can - not make your own__ corn - bread! Sin-gle I____ am,

just__ can't__ tell,____ This__ young man was al-ways well. 2. He
(2) came a big__ frost 'And all____ this young man's corn was lost. 3. He
(4) mar - ry____ me?____ Pret-ty lit-tle miss, what do you say?"
(5) sin-gle I'll re-main,' A la - zy__ man I'll not main-tain.

1, 2, 4, 5

3, 6

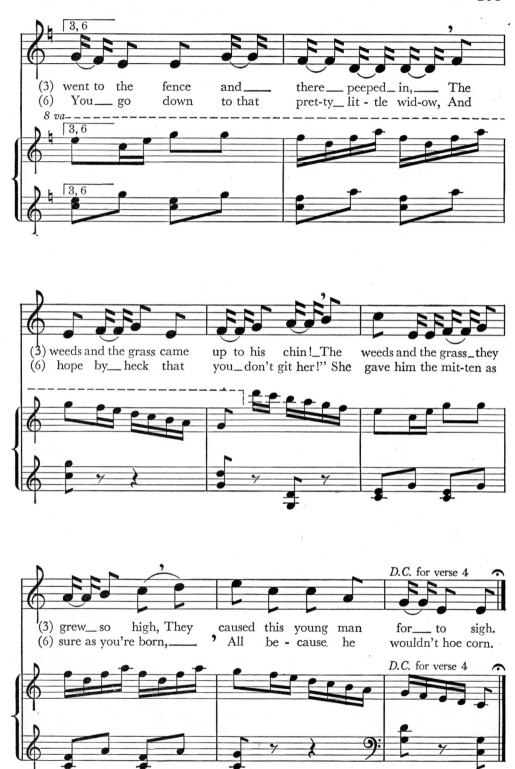

(3) went to the fence and____ there__ peeped_ in,____ The
(6) You__ go down to that pret-ty_ lit - tle wid-ow, And

(3) weeds and the grass came up to his chin!_The weeds and the grass_they
(6) hope by__heck that you__don't git her!" She gave him the mit-ten as

D.C. for verse 4

(3) grew_ so high, They caused this young man for__ to sigh.
(6) sure as you're born,____ All be - cause he wouldn't hoe corn.

D.C. for verse 4

My Love's An Arbutus

A. P. GRAVES   OLD IRISH MELODY

1. My__ love's_an ar - bu - tus By the bor - ders of Lene,
2. But though rud - dy the ber - ry And__ snow - y the flow'r,
3. A - las, fruit and blos - som Shall lie dead__on the lea,

(Humming)

So___ slen - der and__ shape - ly In her gir - dle of green.
That_ bright - en to - geth - er The__ ar - bu - tus bow'r,
And_ Time's jeal - ous__ fin - gers Dim your young charms, Ma-chree,

And I meas - ure   the __ pleas - ure   Of her eye's __ sap - phire __ sheen
Per - fum - ing   and __ bloom-ing   Through __ sun - shine __ and __ show'r,
But un-rang - ing, un - chang-ing,   You'll __ still __ cling __ to __ me,

By the blue __ skies that   spar - kle Through the soft __ branch - ing   screen.
Give __ me __ her bright   lips __ And   her __ laugh's pearl - y   dow'r.
Like the ev - er - green   leaf __ To   the __ ar - bu - tus   tree.

The humming parts can be assigned to instruments and the melody sung by a chorus.

The Swallows Are Homing

ELEANOR FARJEON

CHRISTOS VRIONIDES

1. The swal-lows are hom-ing, The__ swal-lows are hom-ing, The
   sum-mer is com-ing, The__ swal-lows are hom-ing, They're
   swal-lows are hom-ing, The__ swal-lows are hom-ing, The
   sweet is the gloam-ing With__ ap - ple trees bloom-ing, The

brown bee is hum-ming at ev-'ry flow-er's mouth; The
roam-ing, they're roam-ing a - way__ from the south. Oh,__
sum-mer is loom-ing on wood-land and plain; Oh,
swal-lows are hom-ing to Eng - land a- gain. And__

where__ will you nest, You__ first__ of the swal-lows, Be-
nest____ in the shed, Where the cat - tle do__ bed,__ And__
where__ will you nest, You__ sec-ond of the swal-lows? What__
nest____ in the eaves 'Twixt the sound of green__ leaves__ And the

fore the next__ fol-lows, Oh,__ where__will you nest? I will
hear the cows__ low__ As they go____ to their rest. 2. The
ga-bles, what hol-lows Will__ shel - ter you best? I will (To Coda)
coo__ of the child__ On its moth - er's__ breast. The

CODA

swal-lows are hom-ing, The swal-lows are hom-ing, The swal-lows are

hom - ing to Eng-land a - gain, To Eng - land a - gain.

The Scale
(Canon)

LUDWIG VAN BEETHOVEN

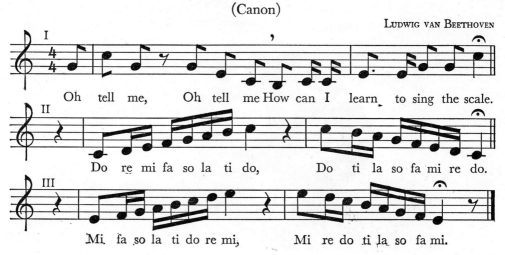

Oh tell me, Oh tell me How can I learn to sing the scale.

Do re mi fa so la ti do, Do ti la so fa mi re do.

Mi fa so la ti do re mi, Mi re do ti la so fa mi.

Holy, Holy

From "THE HOLY CITY" ALFRED R. GAUL

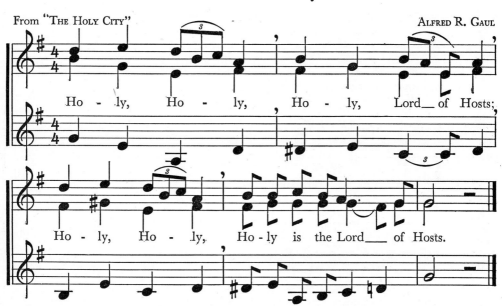

Ho - ly, Ho - ly, Ho - ly, Lord of Hosts;

Ho - ly, Ho - ly, Ho - ly is the Lord of Hosts.

The Triplet. A rhythmic effect which occurs quite often in musical compositions is the triplet. The rhythm is called a triplet when three tones are sounded (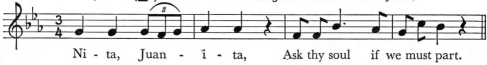) where two tones were expected. A well-known song can illustrate this rhythm:

Ni - ta, Juan - i - ta, Ask thy soul if we must part.

When you find a triplet in a song you are learning, you can refer to this phrase from JUANITA and, by comparing the two, work out the rhythmic effect in the new song.

Aloha Oe
(Farewell to Thee)

Hawaiian Song by
H. M. Queen Liliuokalani

Slowly and with dignity

1. Proud-ly sweeps the rain cloud by the cliffs As
Ha - a - heo e ka u - a i na pa - li Ke

on-ward it glides through the trees; It seems to be fol-low-ing the
ni - hi a - e la i ka-na-he - le E u hai a-na pa-ha i ka

li - ko, The a - hi-hi-le-hu - a of the vale.
li - ko Pu - a a - hi-hi-le-hu - a o u - ka.

CHORUS

(Melody)

Fare - well to thee, fare - well to thee, Thou
A - lo - ha oe, a - lo - ha oe, E ke

200

charm-ing one who dwells a-mong the bow-ers; One fond em-brace___ be-
o - na o - na no-ho i ka, li-po; One fond em-brace___ a

rall.

fore I now de-part,___ Un - til we meet___ a-gain, till we meet a-gain.
ho - i a - e a - u, Un - til we meet___ a-gain, till we meet a-gain.

rall.

2. Thus sweet memories come back to me,
Bringing fresh remembrance of the past;
Dearest one, yes, thou art mine own,
From the true love shall never depart.

O ka halia aloha kai hiki mai
Ke hone ae nei i kuu manawa.
O oe no ka'u ipo aloha
A loko e hana nei.

From KING'S BOOK OF HAWAIIAN MELODIES.
Used by permission of Charles E. King.

O For the Wings of a Dove

202

Paraphrased from Psalm LV

Felix Mendelssohn-Bartholdy

O___ for the wings, _ for the wings__ of a dove! Far a-way, far a-

way would I rove! O___ for the wings, _ for the wings__ of a dove!

Far a-way, far a-way, far a-way, far a-way would__I rove!

In the wil - der-ness build___ me a nest,____ And re-

main__ there for-ev - er at rest, ____ In the wil - der-ness build me,

build me a nest,___ And re - main there for - ev - er at rest,

In___ the wil - der-ness build me a nest,__ And re - main there for-

ev - er at rest, And____ re - main__ there for - ev - er at rest,

And__ re-main__ there for-ev - er at rest.____

Why Are We Waiting

Eleanor Alletta Chaffee

Folk Song from Slovakia

Why are we wait - ing, the sun is high;
Pack up your knap-sack with things to eat;

Morn-ing is spread-ing a - cross the sky.
For - ests are wait - ing for ea - ger feet.

Free as the swal - low, On-ward we fol - low,
This is a play day, Hap-py and gay day,

There are a hun-dred new trails to try.
Man - y sur - pris - es we'll sure - ly meet!

Free as the swal - low, On-ward we fol - low,
This is a play day, Hap-py and gay day,

There are a hun-dred new trails to try.
Man - y sur - pris - es we'll sure - ly meet!

Syncopation. In nearly all music the first beat of the measure is accented. In $\frac{4}{4}$ meter the third beat also has a secondary accent. We say that a rhythm is syncopated when these usual accents are shifted, and fall at unexpected places. Syncopation gives life and vigor to musical rhythms. One of the most frequent kinds of syncopation is very familiar:

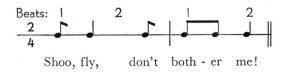

Beats: 1   2   1   2

Shoo, fly,   don't both - er me!

The Dove
(La Paloma)

Sebastian Yradier

The day___ that I left my home for the roll-ing sea,___
And when ___ I come home, from Ni-na to part no more,___
Cuan - do___ sa - lí de la Ha-ba-na, ¡vál - ga - me Dios!___

I said,___ "Moth-er dear, oh, pray to thy God for me."___
To rest,___ with my moth-er dear, on my na - tive shore,___
Na - die___ me ha vis - to sa - lir___ si no fuí yo___

And then___ ere we sailed, I went a fond leave to take___
A - dieu___ to the ship where of-ten with chang - ing mind,___
Y u - na___ lin-da gua-chi - nan-ga a - llá voy yo___

Of Ni - na who wept as though her poor heart would break.
I've laughed___ and I've wept as veered the light, chang-ing wind.
Que se___ vi - no tras de mí___ que sí se - ñor.

Ni - na, if I should die and o'er o - cean's foam___
Then comes the day, the hap - py and bless - ed day___
Si a tu ven - ta - na lle - ga u - na pa - lo - ma.___

Soft - ly a white dove on a fair eve should come,___
Chas-ing all sad - ness, sor-row and care a - way;___
trá - ta - la con ca - ri - ño que es mi per - so - na.___

All Round the Mountain

SOUTH CAROLINA PLANTATION SONG
Collected by MARSHALL BARTHOLOMEW

All round the moun-tain, charm-ing Bet - sy,⎯⎯

All round the moun-tain, Lau - ra Lee,⎯⎯

If I nev - er see her no more,

May the good Lawd re - mem - ber me.⎯⎯

1. Town gal,⎯⎯ she rides an au - to - mo - bile,⎯⎯
2. Town gal,⎯⎯ she wears a sat - in⎯⎯ dress,⎯⎯
3. Town gal,⎯⎯ she wears⎯⎯ high - heel⎯⎯ shoes,⎯⎯

Coun-try gal,⎯⎯ she rides the same,⎯⎯
Coun-try gal,⎯⎯ she wears the same,⎯⎯
Coun-try gal,⎯⎯ she wears the same,⎯⎯

Moun - tain gal rides an old ox - cart,⎯⎯
Moun - tain gal wears a cal - i - co dress,⎯⎯
Moun - tain gal wears⎯⎯ no shoes at all,⎯⎯

But she gets there just the same.⎯⎯

Fashions

(*Anquinhās*)

Adapted from the original PORTUGUESE by
ELLEN WALES WALPOLE

BRAZILIAN POPULAR SONG
In the rhythm of a HABANERA
Arranged by HEITOR VILLA-LOBOS

A fash-ion pa-rade is show-ing, All the
such a su-perb col-lec-tion It is
Á mo-do das taes an-quin-has, E' una

*Tum tum tum tum, Tum tum tum tum,

col-ors are bright and glow-ing, Though may-be not so con-
awk-ward to make se-lec-tion, For fash-ions with style once
mo-da es-tran-gu-la-da. De-pois de joe-lho em

Tum tum tum tum, Tum tum tum tum, Tum tum tum tum,

struct-ive, Styles most cer-tain-ly are ef-fec-tive! From
load-ed Are as sure-ly to-day out-
ter-ra. Faz a gen-te fi-car pas-ma-da.

mod-ed!
ma-da.

Tum tum tum tum, Tum tum tum tum tum, Tum! Tum! *O-lé!*

* Imitating a guitar.

The little syncopated rhythmic figure ♩♪♩ is much used in Spanish music and in the music of countries where the Spanish influence is strong, such as Latin America and the Caribbean Islands. Debussy uses this rhythm in his humorous "Golliwogg's Cake-Walk." (See page 159.)

Merry Medley

Throughout this medley the melody is in the second part and will be sung by most of the pupils. A few high, light voices are to sing the upper part, called a "counter-part." This part differs from a descant in that a descant is an independent melody which contrasts with the principal song; whereas a counter-part is purely harmonic. In popular music it is often called a "tenor." The third part is to be sung only by pupils who can sing deep tones easily; if there are no deep voices in the class, the part may be omitted.

(Melody)

I've been work- in' on the rail - road, All the live - long day;

I've been work-in' on the rail - road, Just to pass the time a - way.

Don't you hear the whis-tles blow-ing, Rise up so ear-ly in the morn;

Don't you hear the cap-tain shout - ing: "Di - nah, blow your horn!"

Hear them bells, don't you hear them bells, They are

ring-ing out the glo-ry of the Lord. Hear them bells, don't you

hear them bells, They are ring-ing out the glo-ry of the Lord.

Solo The Camp-town la-dies sing this song, Chorus Doo- dah, Doo-dah,

Solo The Camp-town race-track five miles long, Chorus Oh, doo- dah - day!

I come down here with my hat caved in, Doo-dah, Doo-dah,

I go back home with a pock-et full of tin,

Oh, Doo-dah - day! Goin' to run all night, Goin' to run all

day, I'll___ bet my mon-ey on the bob - tail nag,

some-bod-y bet on the bay! Mer - ri - ly we roll a - long,

Roll a - long, roll a - long, Mer - ri - ly we roll a - long,

O'er the deep blue sea. Good night, la - dies, Good night, la - dies,

Good night, la - dies, We're going to leave you now.

Mer - ri - ly we roll a - long, roll a - long, roll a - long,

Mer - ri - ly we roll a - long, O'er the deep blue sea.

212

Baked Potato
(*Tan' patat'-la cuite*)

Paraphrased from the original by
JANE ROLFE RANDOLPH

CREOLE SONG
from LOUISIANA

A baked po-ta-to burns the fin-gers, Care-ful, be-cause it's hot!____ A
I'm goin' to have that baked po-ta-to Meal-y and plump and hot,____ I'm
Et tan' pa-tat'-la cuit' ma man-gé li-i ma man-gé li.____ Et

Baked po-ta-to!

baked po-ta-to burns the fin-gers, Care-ful, be-cause it's hot!____
goin' to grab that baked po-ta-to, Meal-y and plump and hot!____
tan' pa-tat'-la cuit' ma man-gé li-i ma man-gé li.____

Baked po-ta-to!

(MELODY)
Look out, it's on the coals!____ Look out, it's in the flame!____
Wheth-er it's on the coals,____ Wheth-er it's in the flame,____
Tan' même li dan' chau-dière,____ Tan' même li dan' la cend,____

Baked po-ta-to! Baked po-ta-to!

Bet-ter be slow with baked po-ta-to, Trou-ble, if you are not!____
I'm goin' to grab that baked po-ta-to, Gob-ble it on the spot!____
Tan' même li dan' du feu ma man-gé, Li-i ma man-gé li.____

The third voice-part is excellent for the lower tones of boys' voices.

Snare Drum

Tempo di Bolero moderato assai

Two quotations from the
opening measures of "BOLERO"
by MAURICE RAVEL (1875-1937)

and so on

Flute

pp

Permission granted by Durand & Cie, Paris
and Elkan-Vogel Co., Inc., Philadelphia, Pa.,
Copyright Owners

When we listen to music written by the outstanding composers of our own times we cannot fail to notice how they delight in striking rhythmic variety, in novel melodies, and in harmonies filled with clashing dissonances. Compositions which a few years ago would have seemed utterly meaningless are now enjoyed by the general public. We are no longer disturbed by discords or distressed by melodies which rush from one tonality to another. However, we do require the composer to have a real plan and purpose in what he has to say, and skill in expressing himself. Even the composers of our lighter popular music must fall into the spirit of this new expression, or we think of their music as commonplace.

One of the most distinguished composers of our own times is Maurice Ravel, who is universally acclaimed as an outstandingly great musician. He has written a large number of splendid works, many of which seem likely to continue on concert programs for a long time. In 1928 he composed his remarkable "Bolero," which startled the musical world by its novel plan and unusual melodic and rhythmic effects. Written originally as ballet music and produced in that manner at the Paris Opéra, it was published the following year as an orchestral selection. Throughout the composition the snare drum persistently plays a striking rhythmic figure, while over it the other instruments play a strange, haunting melody. The "Bolero" begins quietly and works up to a tremendous climax.

Tending the Sheep

ELLEN WALES WALPOLE

FRENCH-CANADIAN FOLK SONG

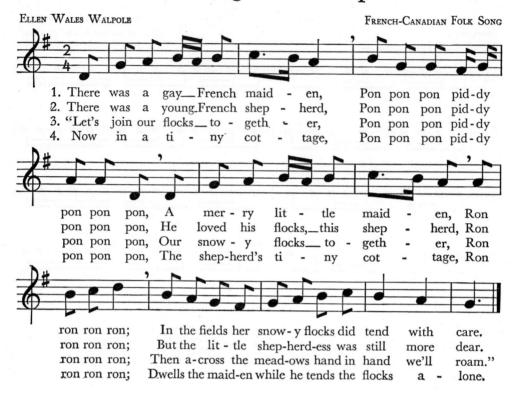

1. There was a gay—French maid - en, Pon pon pon pid-dy
2. There was a young—French shep - herd, Pon pon pon pid-dy
3. "Let's join our flocks— to - geth - er, Pon pon pon pid-dy
4. Now in a ti - ny cot - tage, Pon pon pon pid-dy

pon pon pon, A mer - ry lit - tle maid - en, Ron
pon pon pon, He loved his flocks,—this shep - herd, Ron
pon pon pon, Our snow - y flocks— to - geth - er, Ron
pon pon pon, The shep-herd's ti - ny cot - tage, Ron

ron ron ron; In the fields her snow-y flocks did tend with care.
ron ron ron; But the lit - tle shep-herd-ess was still more dear.
ron ron ron; Then a-cross the mead-ows hand in hand we'll roam."
ron ron ron; Dwells the maid-en while he tends the flocks a - lone.

Herons Homeward Flying

Text adapted from the
HUNGARIAN of BÉNE EGRESSY
by MARTIN HERNE

HUNGARIAN FOLK SONG
used by FRANZ LISZT in
HUNGARIAN RHAPSODY No. 14

Her - ons fly-ing, home-ward fly-ing, wings out-spread. Long-ing fills me
Far the coun-try where the riv-er takes its course. Would that south-ward

while I watch them o - ver - head. Fly-ing south-ward where a gen-tle
I were rid-ing on my horse. Or like her-ons fly-ing south-ward

maid I know Sad - ly wan-ders by the riv-er whose clear wa-ters
through the blue I might greet her by the wa-ters, greet the maid-en

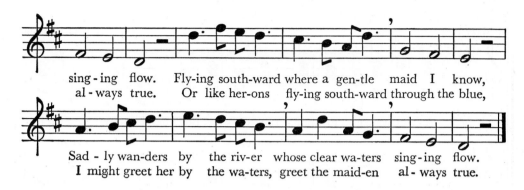

sing-ing flow.   Fly-ing south-ward where a gen-tle   maid I   know,
al-ways true.   Or like her-ons   fly-ing south-ward through the blue,

Sad-ly wan-ders by   the riv-er whose clear wa-ters sing-ing flow.
I might greet her by   the wa-ters, greet the maid-en   al-ways true.

Go, Tell It On the Mountain

NEGRO SPIRITUAL

1. When I   was   a   seek-er   I   sought both night and   day,   I
2. He made me   a   watch-man Up-on   the cit-y   wall, And
3. In   the time of   Da-vid Some said he was a   king. And

asked the Lord to   help me   And   He shows me   the   way.____
if   I   serve Him tru-ly   I   am   the least of   all.____
if   a   child is   true born The Lord will hear him sing.____

(Melody)
Go   tell   it on   the moun-tains,   O-ver the hills and   ev-'ry-where,

Go   tell   it on   the moun-tains, Our heav'n-ly Lord___ is born.

Vacation

From the NORWEGIAN of P. A. JENSEN
by MARY BUDLONG

J. G. CONRADI

A - way we'll go to - mor - row Up - on our hol - i - day,_____ With-
a-way,

out a care_ or sor - row We'll soon be on_our way,_____ O,
a-way.

gold-en hours of play-time! We lift our hearts in song,_ As free as birds in
in song,

May-time; Come join the hap-py throng, Come join the hap-py_ throng!_

A Pirate Ship
(Ballymena)

ANNA M. SHEPARD

FOLK SONG from the BAHAMAS

Bal-ly - me - na, Bal-ly - me - na, Bal-ly - me - na in the har-bor,
(1-3)
(4) o-cean,

Bal-ly - me - na, Bal-ly - me - na, Bal-ly - me - na, in the har-bor.
(1-3)
(4) o-cean.

1. Bring the *Bal - ly - me - na*, Bring her to the dock and
2. Bring the skull and cross - bones, Nail it to the mast - head,
3. Fit her up with big sails, Arm her to the gun - wales,[1]
4. Met a man - o' - war, then, With a hun - dred can - non,

Paint the *Bal - ly - me - na* black.
Then good-by to Un - ion Jack.
Man her with a pi - rate crew.
Ba - la, oh fare-well to you!

1, 2, 3,   4. *D. C. al Fine*

Bal - ly - me - na!

* The small notes to be sung by a few voices in the last stanza only.

[1] Pronounced *gun-els.*

218 Here By Friendship Firm United

A. J. FOXWELL

W. A. MOZART

1. Here by friend - ship firm u - nit - ed,
2. Let us praise the great Cre - a - tor,
3. Those on earth will best o - bey Him,

Hand in hand we join de - light - ed,
Lord of all the pow'rs of na - ture.
Who by faith and truth re - pay Him

Raised by love to thoughts sub - lime!
Praise Him for His wise de - cree,
For His grace and good - ness shown.

Hearts thus weld - ed naught can sev - er;
Mak - 'ing faith and truth the meas - ure
Love to God and man are blend - ed

Vir - tue's bond will last for - ev - er;
Of our earth - ly joy and pleas - ure.
In each kind - ly act ex - tend - ed.

Stead - fast through the storms____ of time.
Lead . ing us from, ill_____ to flee.
These He ev er deigns____ to own.

(When there are no instruments, this line may be hummed.)

The Star-Spangled Banner

(Service Version)

FRANCIS SCOTT KEY

JOHN STAFFORD SMITH

An Act of Congress, approved March 3, 1931, made "The Star-Spangled Banner" the national anthem of the United States of America.

1. Oh,— say! can you see,— by the dawn's ear - ly light, What so proud - ly we hailed at the twi - light's last gleam-ing? Whose broad stripes and bright stars through the per - il - ous fight, O'er the ram - parts we watched were so gal - lant - ly

2. On the shore, dim - ly seen— through the mists of the deep, Where the foe's haugh-ty host in dread si - lence re-pos - es, What is that which the breeze, o'er the tow - er - ing steep, As it fit - ful - ly blows, half con - ceals, half dis-

3. Oh,— thus be it ev - er when— free - men shall stand Be - tween their loved homes and the war's des - o - la - tion! Blest with vic - t'ry and peace, may the heav'n - res - cued land Praise the Pow'r that hath made and pre-served us a

stream - ing? And the rock - ets' red glare, the bombs burst - ing in
clos - es? Now it catch - es the gleam of the morn - ing's first
na - tion! Then___ con - quer we must, when our cause it is

air, Gave___ proof through the night___ that our flag was still there.
beam, In full glo - ry re - flect - ed now___ shines on the stream;
just; And___ this___ be our mot - to: "In___ God is our trust!"

CHORUS

Oh,___ say, does that___ Star - Span - gled Ban - ner ___ yet___
'Tis the Star - Span - gled___ Ban - ner, oh long may___ it___
And the Star - Span - gled___ Ban - ner, in tri - umph___ shall___

wave___ O'er the land___ of the free and the home of the brave?
wave___ O'er the land___ of the free and the home of the brave!
wave___ O'er the land___ of the free and the home of the brave!

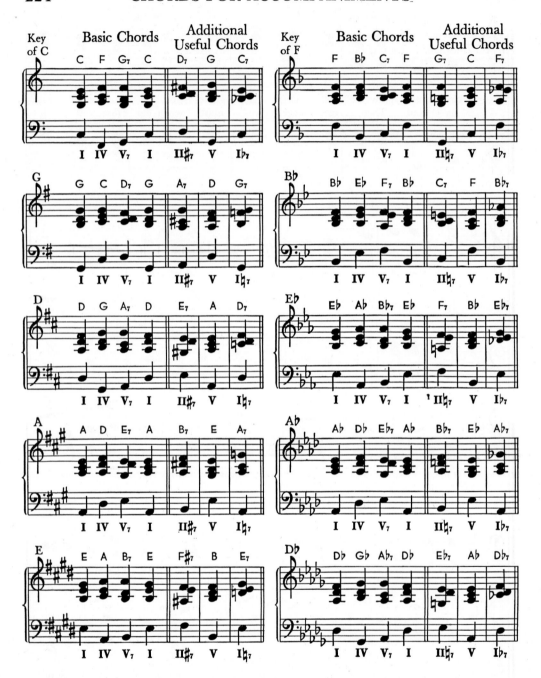

Chording in minor keys will be found in this book on the following pages:

C minor — pp. 114, 174

A minor — p. 114

F minor — p. 121

G minor — p. 178

Most folk songs and other familiar songs are based on simple harmonies.   On p. 224 you
   will find nearly every chord needed to play piano accompaniments for many of the songs
   you know.   Below, these chords are shown in various rhythms which will add interest to
   the music and will express different moods.   In each measure pattern, $\frac{2}{4}$ $\frac{3}{4}$ $\frac{4}{4}$ and $\frac{6}{8}$, there
   are four distinct styles of chording: a, b, c, and d.   Just for fun, try these measure pat-
   terns with some of the chord successions on p. 224.   Then try to use these chords in
   making up your own accompaniments to your favorite songs.

After you have become used to playing chords in this manner, you can try another plan.   Play
   a familiar melody with your right hand, and a chord accompaniment with your left hand.   If
   you begin with something simple you can soon figure out how this is done.

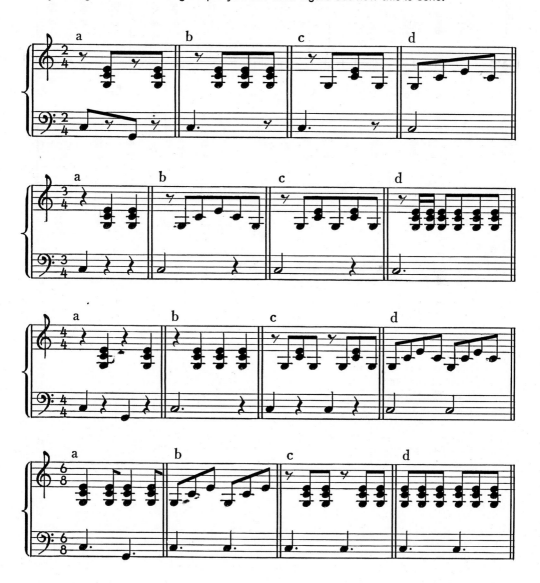

America

Henry Carey

1. My country! 'tis of thee,
   Sweet land of liberty,
   Of thee I sing;
   Land where my fathers died,
   Land of the Pilgrims' pride,
   From ev'ry mountain side
   Let freedom ring.

2. My native country, thee,
   Land of the noble free,
   Thy name I love;
   I love thy rocks and rills,
   Thy woods and templed hills,
   My heart with rapture thrills
   Like that above.

3. Let music swell the breeze,
   And ring from all the trees
   Sweet Freedom's song;
   Let mortal tongues awake,
   Let all that breathe partake,
   Let rocks their silence break,
   The sound prolong.

4. Our fathers' God, to Thee,
   Author of liberty,
   To Thee we sing;
   Long may our land be bright
   With Freedom's holy light;
   Protect us by Thy might,
   Great God, our King.

Samuel Francis Smith

In the Fifth Book you were shown how a hymn tune, written for four voice parts on two staves, may be condensed so as to become playable by small hands. When grown-up musicians play hymn tunes on the piano, they customarily play the bass in octaves and play the other three tones of the chord in close harmony with the right hand. This gives greater power for accompanying group singing. It requires some experience to condense the tones for the right hand, but practice in this style is most rewarding, both in effective playing and in increased musicianship. AMERICA is here shown in this kind of arrangement.

USING THE SIXTH BOOK IN THE CLASSROOM

The Sixth Book of NEW MUSIC HORIZONS provides the capstone to the music study plan in the elementary grades and, at the same time, previews the objectives attainable in the seventh and eighth grades. The songs cover a wide variety of interests, from the infectious humor of our pioneer ancestors to the great art songs of the masters. Particular stress is laid on world brotherhood, and characteristic songs of many peoples carry their spirit into the classroom. The five-fold program of music activities and experiences is continued through Singing, Playing, Dancing, Listening, and Creating. The material for further development of skill in music reading is selected for its intrinsic musical merit and interest as well as for its appropriate place in the study program. Pictures which illumine the spirit of the songs give further emphasis to the art program of the series and to the plan of creative interpretation. The song texts include many gems from the famous poets of our own country and England as well as authentic and artistic translations from other languages.

Several important developments will be noticed:

(1) Three-part singing is introduced through a functional, creative approach, with ample easy material to provide for rich experience. Instrumental and vocal chording combine to strengthen the pupils' harmonic consciousness. Pupils learn to think tones in harmonic combination as well as in melodic succession.

(2) Songs in minor tonality have been included in the experience of children from the earliest grades. In the Sixth Book conscious study is given to music in the minor keys, as is shown in the outlines under Music Reading.

(3) Increasing emphasis is given to socializing the music program by making it possible for every pupil to contribute his share to the class performance in the medium individually most interesting to him. More and more, the pupils' school music experience may be brought into the home and community. The so-called recreational instruments are encouraged both for their own values and as a means of awakening interests which may be broadened through further experience.

(4) The section on Radio is included in the hope that with a clearer picture of what a radio program involves, more purposeful listening to radio may result.

In every way the Sixth Book aims to displace the old, stereotyped music lesson with a vital and functional program that will bring music into the schoolroom, home, and community as a permanent and happy life experience.

I. EXPRESSIVE SINGING

In the Sixth Book the singing program falls under six headings:

1. Voice Compass. The songs have been selected and the keys chosen with careful attention to the use of the voices of girls and boys of sixth grade level.

2. Tone Quality. The pupils should be made conscious of the importance of singing with beautiful tone, in order to express the moods and meanings of the songs which they sing. The vocal tone should be colored by the spirit of the song, thus linking closely considerations of tone quality with creative interpretation.

3. Special Voice Pages. In the Fifth Book emphasis was given to the proper production of the "Root Vowels," ah, $\bar{o}$, $\overline{oo}$, $\bar{a}$, $\bar{e}$. The pupils should realize that good tone quality depends on the way vowels are sung, and in all their singing should maintain this as one of their chief aims.

In the Sixth Book, p. 139, an excellent device is suggested for sustaining a smooth and even tone while pronouncing the words distinctly. The words are sung on one tone, with clear articulation of the consonants but without a break in the sustained tone. This is then applied in singing other songs.

4. Songs Great Artists Sing. At no time in his life is the unchanged soprano voice of a boy more beautiful than at the sixth or seventh grade level. Girls' voices, too, are often peculiarly lovely at this age. It is a time when special attention may be given to singing with fine tone quality, careful phrasing, and distinct pronunciation. These are the skills which all great singers strive to cultivate. Several songs included in the Sixth Book have frequently appeared on the programs of great artists and are everywhere recognized as among the most beautiful examples of song literature. See pp. 5, 32, 96, 118, 188, 202. There are, of course, many other lovely songs in the Sixth Book which invite the greatest attention to beauty of tone and expressive interpretation.

5. Part Singing.

a. Voice parts. Although all pupils should be encouraged to sing upper, middle, or lower voice parts, occasionally individual voices will be found that have so limited a range that they must be assigned permanently to one or two of the voice parts. Even so, the pupil should be offered every inducement to sing over as wide a voice compass as is comfortable.

b. Vocal chording. Several songs are especially adapted to an accompaniment of vocal chording. See pp. 26, 63, 74. Vocal chording in various keys provides excellent training in thinking harmonically, in securing purity of intonation, and in tone blending.

c. Harmonic and contrapuntal part singing. On page 23 a distinction is drawn between two different styles of part singing: harmonic and contrapuntal. This distinction is a great aid in determining both the approach to the study of the song, and also the manner in which the song may be sung most effectively.

Among the many examples of each type of song, the following may be noted: 1. Harmonic: pp. 11, 18, 26, 27, 39, 42, 52, 142, 200, 208, 218, and numerous others. 2. Contrapuntal (or both): pp. 22, 23, 10, 34, 55, 71, 127, 146, 176, 180, 196, and many others.

6. Preparation for the change in Boys' Voices. Classes differ as to the time when maturing of the boy's voice may be expected. However, where the actual change is least in evidence, there is a sturdiness of physique and an increased fullness of tone noticeable in the voices of sixth grade boys. In the Sixth Book this condition has been taken into account in two ways: a. A number of songs are available which are especially adapted to this type of boy's voice, and which boys will delight in singing. See pp. 8, 60, 61, 92, 130, 132b, 139, 146, 160, 168, 192, 203, 206, 217.

b. The arrangement of three-part songs utilizes the rich lower tones of the boys' voices without confining them to too limited compass and without excessive employment of the lowest tones. See pp. 27, 35, 36, 46a, 46b, 62, 79, 123, 134, 140, 142, 149, 154, 184, 200, 212.

II. PLAYING AN INSTRUMENT

The instrumental program, as developed in the earlier books of the course finds rich fruition in the Sixth Book. The program is designed to (a) provide all pupils with a minimum background of information concerning certain of the more important musical instruments; (b) encourage pupils to take up the study of some instrument; (c) utilize playing on percussion instruments in the expanded programs of music reading, dancing, and listening; (d) socialize the music program by encouraging each pupil to participate in the general ensemble in the way that he will enjoy most and to the degree that he will profit most.

A. Drum Music. The extremely useful device of drumming the accents, beats, and note patterns was extensively developed in the earlier books of the course. The teacher may refer to its use in the Fifth Book for classes where a review of the fundamentals of time keeping is desirable. On page 152 a brief excerpt from Haydn's celebrated "Toy" Symphony illustrates the valuable experience in playing percussion instruments from notation. The training in time keeping, counting rests, and the feeling of ensemble is invaluable.

B. Piano.

1. Keyboard space-frame. The practice of using the space-frame of the piano keyboard or bells to learn tonal relations in different major and minor keys and to build the scales in these keys, is warmly recommended. This is one of the surest means for developing accuracy in music reading of pitch relations. See pp. 2, 30, 38.

2. Chording. The experience in chording on the piano and other appropriate instruments introduced in the Fifth Book is continued throughout the Sixth Book, and a number of songs include chord lettering. The plan for finding these chords is reviewed on page 9. The more usual chords are given in ten keys on page 224. The chords in minor keys will be found on the following pages: C minor, pp. 114, 174; A minor, p. 114; F minor, p. 121; G minor, p. 178.

3. Piano accompaniments, as given in the Sixth Book, are of four types. (a) Chordings for accompaniments are marked on a number of songs. On page 225 suggestions are given for playing these chords in various rhythms, thereby adding interest to the music and expressing different moods. This experience will lead to playing the melody with one hand and the chords with the other hand. (b) Simple piano accompaniments are provided for the songs on pages 20 (dance), 108, 152 (score), 218. These are intended to encourage pupils who play the piano to participate in the class performance of these songs, and then to play the accompaniments of other songs as given in the Accompaniment Book. (c) A few art songs include piano accompaniments where the piano is an essential part of the composition. See pp. 74, 106, 150, 162, 194. (d) On page 226 the playing of hymn tunes is discussed as a help to pupils who are interested in accompanying four-part vocal music in the school, Sunday school, and home.

C. Social, or Recreational Instruments. Certain musical instruments are widely used for playing music and accompanying singing for social and recreational occasions. In the hands of talented performers, some of these instruments are capable of artistic musical expression, though usually they are associated with music for purely social enjoyment. In a democratic program of music education, which recognizes the right of all pupils to participate in music on the level of their individual capacities and interests, these instruments have a legitimate place. This is true both for their own values and also as steps toward broader musical interests. Under the heading of social, or recreational instruments may be included the harmonica, accordion, pipes, and the fretted instruments, such as guitar, banjo, bandello, lute, ukulele, and mandolin. For the songs in the Sixth Book which appropriately may be played by some of these instruments, see pp. 12, 52, 57b, 81, 140, 141, 160, 169, 173, 182, 200, 204, 208, and 217.

D. Instruments of the Orchestra and Band. These lessons are designed to awaken an interest in instrumental performance, both as players and as listeners. Pupils who play, both members of the class and those from higher grades, may play along with the singers in socialized vocal and instrumental ensembles.

Violin: pp. 25, 152, 180, 191; Fiddle tunes: pp. 44, 126; Cello: pp. 25, 45, 152, 218; String Bass: pp. 45, 152; Flute: pp. 29, 213; Clarinet: p. 1; Cornet or Trumpet: p. 1; Tuba: p. 66; Harp: p. 116; Drums, etc.: pp. 29, 213; Percussion: pp. 62, 152; Ensembles: pp. 1, 20, 152, 218; Obbligatos: pp. 34, 64, 127, 180, 182, 196.

E. Supplementary Instrumental Material. In order that the class music experiences may be socialized by making it possible for every pupil to participate according to his own preferences and talents, instrumental material of three types has been prepared from the books of the series.

1. Arrangements for instruments of the orchestra and band. Songs, dances, and listening selections are available, arranged so that any number of players may join in performing them on any group of instruments, with or without singers. This makes it possible to play these selections in school, home, or community gatherings.

2. Piano arrangements of a number of songs are available in easy arrangements for playing in school or at home.

3. Percussion instruments. A number of songs have been provided with accompaniments for percussion instruments similar to the plan of Haydn's celebrated "Toy" Symphony. These selections are among those in the orchestra album, but may also be played with only piano or singers. They offer enjoyable musical experience and invaluable training in music reading.

III. RHYTHMIC ACTIVITIES

Where the program of rhythmic activities has been followed consistently through the earlier grades, the material in the Sixth Book offers opportunities for a wealth of pleasurable experiences. Most of the social dances are familiar and will be reviewed with enthusiasm. The few that are new are attractive as dances and interesting in connection with the social program. The American Longways, Circle, and Square dances are growing rapidly in popularity, and their revival indicates a healthy reaction from some of the modern ballroom dancing. Many of the dances in the Sixth Book lend themselves admirably to dramatization and pageantry. The principal new development will be found in the Creative Floor Patterns as discussed below.

A. Social and National Dances:
March: pp. 1, 13, 29, 40, 168; Waltz: pp. 12, 19a, 52, 87, 95, 116; Polka: pp. 20, 171, 172; Mazurka: p. 31; Minuet: p. 46; Gavotte: p. 98; Polonaise: p. 164; Bolero: p. 213; Longways, Square, and Circle Dances: pp. 44, 88, 125, 126, 191.

B. Creative Floor Patterns. In the dances in the Fifth Book the study of floor patterns was directed chiefly to consideration of design, emphasis being given to the correlation of dance design and the structural organization of the music. The value of this study was chiefly in its relationship to meaningful music reading and intelligent listening to music. The Sixth Book progresses to the creation of floor patterns by the pupils. This is a distinct step in the direction of an understanding and feeling for the modern dance. See page 21.

IV. LISTENING

In the Fourth and Fifth Books of NEW MUSIC HORIZONS emphasis was placed on "listening to learn." Pupils studying the Sixth Book are mature enough to follow with interest the various ways in which music expresses the action, the story, the design, or the mood intended by the composer. Themes are given from typical compositions, with annotations somewhat like those found in the program notes for recitals and concerts. They will show the pupil how backgrounds may be developed for more discriminating and pleasurable listening to music at performances,

over the radio, or from recordings.

p. 25 *Design in Music*
Themes: Contra-Dance No. 1 — Ludwig van Beethoven
The objectives in this lesson are: Recognition of repetition and contrasts of themes, and analysis of period structure by numerals: I, II, etc.

p. 45 *Thematic Development*
Themes: The "Unfinished" Symphony (First Movement) —Franz Schubert
The first movement of Schubert's delightful symphony is based on three principal themes. The ways in which these themes are treated, and the pleasure of recognizing them in their many transformations, is the essence of the forward step in this listening lesson.

p. 66 *The Tuba*
Theme: Introduction, Act III, "Lohengrin"— Richard Wagner
Pupils will readily recognize this striking theme as they listen to the composition. A discussion of the tone of the tuba will lead to a study of tone qualities and expressive characteristics of other orchestral instruments in this and in other selections.

p. 82 *A Strange Coincidence*
Theme: Song of the Mermaid, from the opera, "Oberon"—Carl Maria von Weber
Theme: Overture, "Midsummer Night's Dream" —Felix Mendelssohn-Bartholdy
The similarity in these two notable themes will lead to a discussion of melodic similarities in other compositions, and of originality in old and contemporary music.

p. 95 *Two Composers Use the Same Themes*
Themes: España Waltz—Emile Waldteufel
Today's popular composers frequently turn to the classics for themes for their song hits. Waldteufel's waltz, in which he used the themes from Chabrier's "España," is an early example of this same practice. Is there any justification for such revamping of established musical masterpieces?

p. 116 *The Harp*
Theme: Waltz of the Flowers, "Nutcracker" Suite—Peter I. Tschaikowsky
This is one of the best examples of the harp in a brilliant cadenza. The harp is effective also as an accompanying instrument. Do you know any radio program which features the harp?

p. 159 *Departure from Old Traditions*
Theme: Clair de lune—Claude Debussy
Theme: Golliwogg's Cake-Walk — Claude Debussy
Theme: Valse Triste—Jean Sibelius
The break with the traditions of the classical and romantic composers, which occurred during the closing years of the nineteenth century and the early years of the twentieth century, ushered in the era of modern music. This is typified by the selections on page 159. In what ways do these works express the departure from old traditions?

p. 172 *From Folk Song to Symphony*
Song: Which Shall It Be?—Czech Folk Song
Haydn's use of this melody in the Finale of his Symphony in D Major serves as an excellent way of introducing a movement of a symphony into the listening program.

p. 213 *Music of Our Times*
Themes: Bolero—Maurice Ravel
This novel and striking study in rhythms, tone colors, and climax is an excellent example of con-

temporary musical expression. **Do** you know another modern composition, and can you discover the features which make it distinctive? See also the footnote on page 159.

V. CREATING

Throughout the books of NEW MUSIC HORIZONS, the approach to practically all music activities has been in the creative spirit. These activities should be the outcome of individual initiative, and the personal expression of the pupils. Creative interpretation, adding original stanzas, creative rhythmic activities, creative instrumentation, and creative listening continue to be important phases of the program in the Sixth Book. An example of class activity in original composition appears on page 59. Certain of the pupils will now begin to show individual interest and possibly some talent for composing little songs and instrumental pieces, and will volunteer to prepare such material for appropriate occasions. This is to be encouraged. See also p. 19.

The practice of chording will encourage some pupils to prepare accompaniments to original and familiar melodies, or even to attempt vocal harmonization. Music, more and more, should become a socialized expression to which each pupil offers his best contribution in accordance with his individual talents and interests.

VI. MUSIC READING

The music reading program of NEW MUSIC HORIZONS is based on the ideal that our pupils should know many beautiful songs and that they should learn them quickly and accurately. To accomplish this they must be able to read from music notation. There is so much lovely music to be sung and played, and so much joy to be had through singing, playing, and dancing, that we cannot afford to waste time because of lack of reading ability. Neither can we afford to waste time in anything less than the quickest and most efficient ways of acquiring music reading skill.

The Fourth and Fifth Books of NEW MUSIC HORIZONS carried forward a music reading program which aimed at the development of skill in the use of music notation in learning new songs. This program included a variety of approaches, thus enabling the teacher to offer the pupils several different kinds of reading experience, out of which each child could find his own most effective means for acquiring reading skill. The Sixth Book provides for the attainment of this program.

A. *Tonal.* The music reading program continues the use of *so-fa* syllables, scale numbers, and pitch names, as preferred by the teacher. The continued use of the piano keyboard (or bells) is also advocated as a functional means for the study of pitch relations in an easily understood "space-frame."

1. Part Singing. NEW MUSIC HORIZONS offers a carefully prepared program for the development of good part singing. Two-part singing is studied in the Fifth Book, following a "readiness" preparation in the Fourth Book. The Fifth Book also presents a "readiness" program for three-part singing in four ways: (1) A few carefully selected three-part rounds; (2) A few examples of three-part harmonies; (3) Two-part songs arranged so that the accompanying voice is sometimes below and sometimes above the principal melody, thus awakening harmonic consciousness; (4) The plan of piano chording giving definite emphasis to the feeling for harmony. The study of three-part singing stems directly from the experiences of this readiness program. The variety of types of three-part songs prevents the study from becoming stereotyped and leads to an acuteness of harmonic hearing which greatly increases the pupil's pleasure and skill. Vocal chording, based on the familiar progressions of piano chording, taken from time to time in connection with the study of new songs, will help in attuning ear and voice to more artistic part singing.

a. Two-part rounds and canons: pp. 2, 7, 10a
b. Rounds and canons in three and more parts: pp. 6, 10b, 16b, 19, 55a, 101, 151, 176, 199a
c. Melody with descant: p. 71
d. Two-part songs: pp. 11, 12, 13, 18, 22, 23, 38, 41, 55b, 57, 58b, 72, 78, 81, 82, 83, 84b, 90, 102a, 102b, 106, 115, 132, 138, 146, 148, 167, 168, 169, 172b, 178, 188, 190, 198, 203, 204, 218
e. Two parts with vocal or instrumental descant: p. 64
f. Vocal chording: pp. 26, 32, 35, 39, 77, 91, 121, 174b
g. Three-part accompaniment of vocal chording: pp. 26, 32, 63, 74, 121, 173, 174b, 178b, 182, 196
h. Three-part songs, harmonic: pp. 4, 27, 35, 36, 37, 39, 40, 42a, 42b, 43, 46a, 46b, 47, 52, 54, 56, 59, 61, 62, 70, 76, 77, 79, 80a, 85, 86, 91, 92, 94, 98, 103, 110, 119, 122, 123, 129, 130a, 131, 134, 140, 141, 142, 144, 149, 154, 158, 166, 170a, 171, 179, 180b, 183, 184, 185, 186, 187, 192, 199b, 200, 208, 212, 215, 216, 217
i. Three parts, melody and double descant for voices or instruments: pp. 34, 127

2. Keys. In the earlier books the pupils studied songs in the nine most usual keys. By using the keyboard approach, the relationship of tones in the scales of these keys became familiar. This study now is reviewed and confirmed by building scales by steps and half-steps, using the keyboard as a measuring rod. When music in a new key is to be studied, a brief review by building its scale according to the formula on page 2 will serve to establish the key.

3. Chromatic Sharps and Flats. Both sharp chromatics and flat chromatics have been presented in the earlier books of the series. In the Sixth Book two additional steps are presented.

(a) Brief Chromatic Progressions in the melody or in an accompanying voice part. Great care must be taken to maintain good intonation either by comparing with an instrument, or by checking with the first and last tones of the chromatic passage. See pp. 102a, 140, 141, and songs throughout later pages in the book.

(b) The Natural. The Natural in music notation has three functions: (1) When the natural appears on a line or space which has been flatted by the key signature, it tells us to sing or play one half-step higher, thus having the function of a sharp. See p. 84a. (2) When the natural appears on a line or space which has been sharped by the key signature, it tells us to sing or play one half-step lower, thus having the function of a flat. See p. 84b. (3) Where an accidental sharp or flat has been used, the natural restores the line or space to its natural pitch. See p. 85.

4. The Bass Clef. In the Fifth Book the bass clef and the relationship of the treble staff and the bass staff were shown in connection with instrumental chording. On page 9 of the Sixth Book this presentation is reviewed, and on page 155 the relationship of the two staves is

again shown in the song "Sailing." While the bass staff at the sixth grade level is still more important in instrumental than in vocal connections, it is quite desirable to have all pupils studying the Sixth Book acquainted with this topic both for present and later application. Boys soon will be singing from the bass staff, and its usefulness in instrumental music will become increasingly important.

5. Music in Minor Keys. In the earlier books of NEW MUSIC HORIZONS a number of rote songs in minor keys have made pupils familiar with this tonal effect. Some of the minor songs are so simple that little difficulty will be met in using them as reading material, even without discussion of minor as a technical study. Such study is presented in the Sixth Book. The materials in the Sixth Book lend themselves to the presentation of the minor mode either as relative or parallel (tonic), depending on the viewpoint or preference of the teacher.

Relative Major and Minor Keys. The traditional presentation of minor songs, particularly where the *so-fa* syllables are used, is by relative keys. In this presentation, the key signature indicates the location of the syllables in both major and minor. In major the keynote is *do;* in minor the keynote is *la.* This is in conformity with the historic use of syllables in sacred chant, where there are different modes in which the keynote may be on any one of the syllables, thereby changing the order of steps and half-steps in the scale and effecting tonal variety. In the course of time secular music reduced these modes to two, our present major and minor keys.

Normal (Natural) Minor. (See Sixth Book, page 112.) By singing songs in normal minor with the *so-fa* syllables the pupils will discover that they usually end on *la.* When we know that a song is in a minor key, *la* may be given as the keynote.

Harmonic Minor. (See Sixth Book, page 114.) The harmonic minor scale is the one most frequently used in building the chords of an accompaniment to a song in the minor mode. This scale differs from the normal minor scale, the minor scale which conforms to the key signature of the composition, in that the seventh tone of the scale appears as a chromatic tone, *si,* and lies one half-step below the eighth, *la.*

In "Chording in the Key of C minor," Sixth Book, page 114, it will be observed that the chords are based on the tones of the harmonic minor scale. For additional chording in minor keys: C minor, page 174; A minor, page 114; F minor, page 121; G minor, page 178.

Scale of E Minor, Melodic Form

1	2	3	4	5	6	7	8	8	7	6	5	4	3	2	1
E	F♯	G	A	B	C♯	D♯	E	E	D♮	C♮	B	A	G	F♯	E
la	ti	do	re	mi	fi	si	la	la	so	fa	mi	re	do	ti	la

Melodic Minor. (See Sixth Book, page 174.) The melodic minor scale offers a smoother upward and downward progression of tones in the upper tetrachord by avoiding the awkward step-and-a-half interval from 6 to 7 as found in the harmonic minor scale. Page 175 of the Sixth Book compares the different forms of the minor scale. It will be observed that the differences lie in the upper tetrachord, and that the lower tetrachord is the same in the three forms, normal, harmonic, and melodic. By writing the Melodic Scale of E minor on the board, the scale pattern may be still further clarified.

Parallel (Tonic) Major and Minor Keys. Although the presentation of vocal music in the minor mode has traditionally been by relative keys, as discussed above, this plan offers serious difficulties when used in instrumental music and in the study of harmony. Many teachers, therefore, present the study of minor by Parallel (Tonic) keys, that is, by using the same keynote for both major and minor scales. When syllables are used in this plan, the keynote always is *do.* This offers difficulties when singing the third and sixth of the scale, some teachers using *me* and *le,* and other teachers using *mi* and *la* but singing a half-step lower than the corresponding tones in the major scale. Many teachers prefer to dispense with syllables altogether, especially in instrumental music, and confine themselves to using numbers and pitch names.

The presentation of the normal, harmonic, and melodic forms of the minor scale, as given on pages 112, 114, and 175 of the Sixth Book, is well adapted to study by playing the scales on a piano keyboard or on bells. The relationship of half-steps, steps, and step-and-a-half intervals is clearly shown and may be used in building scales from any keynote. This plan is also easily adapted to chording, for in major keys the tonic chord (I) and sub-dominant chord (IV) are major (i.e., have a major third in the chord), and in minor keys the tonic chord (i) and sub-dominant chord (iv) are minor (i.e., have a minor third in the chord). The dominant seventh chord (V_7) is the same in both major and minor keys. Compare the chording in minor keys as given in the Sixth Book on pages 114, 121, 174, and 178, with the same chords in parallel major keys.

The pupils discover, as with major keys, that the key signature in minor is derived from the scale pattern as built by using sharps or flats to produce the correct interval progression of the normal minor scale. Many modern composers prefer to dispense with key signatures altogether, and to place sharps and flats wherever necessary to establish the desired tonality. See pp. 150, 162.

Songs based on the Normal Minor Scale: pp. 74, 112, 113a, 113b, 125, 128, 177, 178a.

Songs based on the Harmonic Minor Scale: pp. 114, 115a, 115b, 119, 120a, 120b, 121, 124,

129, 131, 132a, 165, 174b, 185.

Songs based on the Melodic Minor Scale: pp. 174a, 178b, 180, 183.

B. *Rhythmic.* The Fourth and Fifth Books of NEW MUSIC HORIZONS present a plan for developing fluent and accurate reading of rhythmic notation of songs appropriate for that school level. This plan includes: (a) Scansion of the text; (b) Keeping time to the successive beats of the music by the use of strokes, at first straight downward and later in more flowing circles; (c) Drumming the accents, beats, and note patterns; (d) Dancing some of the simpler and more familiar dance rhythms upon which so much of our music is based, in this way approaching music notation with a feeling for the rhythm to be read (the law of expectancy); (e) Stepping the beats while clapping the note patterns, thereby experiencing muscularly the music rhythms as presented by their music notation. These activities should be continued in the Sixth Book wherever they help to clarify the reading situation.

1. Keeping time. (a) Scansion of the text while observing the music notation and beating the time often helps to clarify and simplify the reading of musical rhythms. (b) The Sixth Book offers a study of the universally employed standard process of beating time. The pupils should beat time until it becomes automatic, as an aid for their own music reading, as pupil leaders for the singing of their classmates, and occasionally for conducting experience while listening to recordings of standard instrumental compositions and to the radio. See pages 3, 11, and 56. (c) The device of drumming the accents, beats, and note patterns should be continued and applied consistently until every pupil has mastered the rhythms under consideration and their music notation. (d) Every rhythmic topic presented for study in the reading material of the Sixth Book has previously appeared in rote songs in this book or in earlier books of NEW MUSIC HORIZONS. The rhythm itself, therefore, will not be a new experience when in the development of the reading program its notation comes up for conscious study.

The following list shows where the various rhythms, old and new, are presented and given drill to prepare pupils to read them in subsequent songs:

a. Review of elementary topics of rhythmic notation:

   1. Beat, accent, measure: pp. 3, 11, 56.
   2. Time signatures: pp. 3, 11, 56, 118, 122.
   3. Note and rest values: pp. 10, 118, 122.
   The earlier part of the book includes many simple songs which offer thorough review of the topics presented in the previous books: eighth notes, dotted quarter and eighth notes, six-eight measure, dotted eighth and sixteenth notes.

b. New rhythmic topics in the Sixth Book are:

   1. The eighth-note beat. Sometimes a composer selects the eighth note to represent the value of a beat. See pp. 118, 119. A number of songs in six-eight measure are in a tempo slow enough to give the eighth note the value of a beat, as, for example, pages 115, 128, 130, 138.

   2. The half-note beat. A composer may select the half note to represent the value of a beat. See pp. 122, 123, 130, 132, 139, 168, 179.

   3. Further studies in six-eight measure. Beginning on page 143, the Sixth Book offers a number of songs in six-eight measure in which dotted eighth and sixteenth notes occur. Care has been taken to include only songs in which these rhythms are found in simple relations, and in most cases in slower tempos where the eighth note has the value of a beat. When thoughtfully analyzed these rhythms are not difficult and they are musically most charming. See pp. 143, 148, 160, 165, 166, 186.

   4. Sixteenth note rhythm. Introduced on page 170a, several songs in the later pages of the book include sixteenth note rhythms, i.e., four notes to a beat. See pp. 170a, 172b, 173, 178, 182, 185, 187. Common variants of this rhythm are the eighth note with two sixteenth notes (see pp. 170b, 192, 199, 208), and two sixteenth notes with an eighth note (see pp. 171, 172, 174b, 194, 214).

   5. Syncopation. Two common forms of syncopation are included in the Sixth Book. First is the displacement of the quarter note accent, familiar to us in "ragtime" but also found in folk music of many peoples and used by the great composers. (See Beethoven's "Leonore" Overture No. 3, and Dvořák's "New World" Symphony.) This form of syncopation is introduced on page 203, and is found later on pages 206, 208, 212, 214b, 217. The second form of syncopation is the displacement of the eighth note accent extensively employed in the songs and dances of Latin America. See page 207.

   6. Triplet. The triplet, where three tones are sounded when two are expected, is introduced on page 199 and occurs in songs on pages 202 and 204.

   7. Dance rhythms. Certain of the more familiar and simpler dance rhythms, some of which are basic in instrumental forms, unify the activities of the dance program, the instrumental program, the listening program, and the music reading program. See III. RHYTHMIC ACTIVITIES A.

   8. Stepping-Clapping. This is a valuable activity, and should be used frequently to establish greater accuracy in rhythmic values. The forward flow of the music is maintained by stepping the beats or dance rhythms with the large muscles of the legs. At the same time, by clapping the note patterns with the smaller muscles of the arms and wrists, a balance is secured between the feeling for the swing of the music and its rhythmic details. Songs on the following pages are well adapted to this experience: pp. 2, 3, 6a, 10b, 11, 13, 16b, 41, 57b, 58b, and other songs later in the book.

CLASSIFIED INDEX

234

48

236